Consumer Education and Economics

Fourth Edition

Student Activity Workbook

Ross E. Lowe
Charles A. Malouf
Annette R. Jacobson

New York, New York   Columbus, Ohio   Woodland Hills, California   Peoria, Illinois

Glencoe/McGraw-Hill

A Division of The McGraw-Hill Companies

Copyright © 1997 by Glencoe/McGraw-Hill. All rights reserved. Except as permitted under the United States Copyright Act of 1976, no part of this publication may be reproduced or distributed in any form or by any means, or stored in a database or retrieval system, without prior written permission of the publisher.

Printed in the United States of America.

Send all inquiries to:
Glencoe/McGraw-Hill
21600 Oxnard Street, Suite 500
Woodland Hills, California 91367

ISBN 0-02-637225-8 (Student Edition)
ISBN 0-02-637226-6 (Teacher's Annotated Edition)

6 7 8 9 10 11   066   04 03 02 01 00

Consumer Education and Economics

Contents

UNIT 1 *You and the Economy*

ATTITUDE INVENTORY

Before you begin Unit 1, take stock of your attitudes by completing the following inventory. Read each statement and decide how you feel about it—agree, disagree, or undecided. Write your answers in the blanks.

1. Government agencies offer consumers the best protection against dishonest or misleading selling practices.

   1. _____

2. People should not expect government services unless they are willing to pay for them with higher taxes.

   2. _____

3. Good citizens refrain from using public services and instead rely on themselves.

   3. _____

4. For every consumer right, there is a related responsibility.

   4. _____

5. If businesses would just lower their prices, there would be enough goods and services for everyone, and the businesses themselves would prosper.

   5. _____

6. Government should tax imports in order to protect American products and American jobs.

   6. _____

7. People with higher incomes should pay income taxes at higher rates than people with lower incomes.

   7. _____

8. Entrepreneurs are people who get rich at the expense of consumers.

   8. _____

9. A healthy economic system provides people with low prices and high wages.

   9. _____

10. Income taxes should be raised in order to maintain government services and reduce the federal debt.

    10. _____

11. Federal, state, and local governments spend their tax money on very different things.

    11. _____

12. Gifts of money from one person to another should not be subject to taxation.

    12. _____

RECHECKING YOUR ATTITUDE

Before going on to the next unit, answer the Attitude Inventory questions a second time. Then compare the two sets of responses. On how many statements have your attitudes changed? Can you account for these shifts in your opinions? What do you know now that you did not know then?

1. Government agencies offer consumers the best protection against dishonest or misleading selling practices.

    1. _____

2. People should not expect government services unless they are willing to pay for them with higher taxes.

    2. _____

3. Good citizens refrain from using public services and instead rely on themselves.

    3. _____

4. For every consumer right, there is a related responsibility.

    4. _____

5. If businesses would just lower their prices, there would be enough goods and services for everyone, and the businesses themselves would prosper.

    5. _____

6. Government should tax imports in order to protect American products and American jobs.

    6. _____

7. People with higher incomes should pay income taxes at higher rates than people with lower incomes.

    7. _____

8. Entrepreneurs are people who get rich at the expense of consumers.

    8. _____

9. A healthy economic system provides people with low prices and high wages.

    9. _____

10. Income taxes should be raised in order to maintain government services and reduce the federal debt.

    10. _____

11. Federal, state, and local governments spend their tax money on very different things.

    11. _____

12. Gifts of money from one person to another should not be subject to taxation.

    12. _____

Answers changed _____ Why? _____

_____

_____

_____

_____

_____

_____

_____

_____

_____

_____

_____

_____

CHAPTER 1 *Consumers and the Economy*

REVIEWING CONSUMER TERMS

In a paragraph, define the term *consumer* and then explain the relationship of the following terms to it.

agencies	economics
arbitration service	goods
consumer action panels	redress
consumer affairs department	services
consumer	statutes

_____

_____

_____

_____

_____

_____

_____

_____

_____

_____

_____

_____

_____

_____

_____

_____

_____

_____

_____

_____

_____

_____

_____

_____

_____

_____

_____

_____

CHAPTER 1 *Consumers and the Economy*

REVIEWING FACTS AND IDEAS

1. Which economic roles does a child movie star play? a retired mechanic?

   _____

   _____

   _____

2. Which consumer right (or rights) does each of the statutes listed in Figure 1-3 of your student text protect?

   _____

   _____

   _____

   _____

   _____

   _____

   _____

3. Which federal agency is responsible for:

   a. The safety of cosmetics?

   _____

   b. Meat inspection?

   _____

   c. Truth in advertising?

   _____

4. Name two purposes that consumer action panels serve.

   _____

   _____

   _____

   _____

5. The consumer movement is of recent origin—true or false? Explain.

   _____

   _____

   _____

   _____

   _____

CHAPTER **1** *Consumers and the Economy*

APPLICATION ACTIVITY 1

Mr. Samsoe wanted to buy a small gas grill—the kind with folding legs that can be placed on a tabletop or on a stand. He found just the thing at a super-discount house that dealt mainly in imports. "Portable Gas Grill," the package said in bold letters; and in smaller print, "For outdoor use only." The quality, Mr. Samsoe knew, was not the best, but he planned to use the grill only a few weeks a year and did not want to pay top dollar.

By the time Mr. Samsoe reached the house, a cold, steady rain was falling. Rather than delay using the grill, however, Mr. Samsoe decided to cook his dinner on the grill inside. He reasoned that he could put the grill near an open window, and any smoke would go outside. Mr. Samsoe placed the grill on a table, lighted it, and put his meat on to cook. While he was in the kitchen, one of the legs on the grill folded and the bottom of the grill came into contact with the table, which had a cloth on it to protect its surface. The cloth caught on fire and spread quickly to the rest of the room. Fortunately no one was hurt, but when Mr. Samsoe checked the grill he found that the grill leg was defective. "Products like that aren't safe," he raged. "They shouldn't be sold."

An attorney Mr. Samsoe consulted, however, explained the difficulties of suing a foreign manufacturer. It was expensive and usually a waste of time. He recommended suing the store instead. That did not seem quite right to Mr. Samsoe, but he thought someone should pay for the damage to his house. Reluctantly he agreed.

1. Assume you are Mr. Samsoe. Which of your consumer rights would you argue were violated? Support your choices.

_____

_____

_____

_____

_____

2. Assume you represent the discount store. Which consumer responsibilities would you argue Mr. Samsoe ignored? Support your choices.

_____

_____

_____

_____

_____

_____

_____

CHAPTER 1   Consumers and the Economy

APPLICATION ACTIVITY 2

Read the consumer problems described below. Then identify the federal agency responsible for investigating them.

1. In the last year in your community, there have been three accidents (one of them fatal) involving Shooting Stars, a lawn game sold locally at a number of toy stores. The game's packaging proclaims that Shooting Stars "promotes healthy outdoor activity and is fun for the whole family." An enclosed circular, however, advises that children should not use the product without adult supervision and cautions that the game's weighted projectiles should never be hurled at anything other than the "galaxy rings" provided for that purpose. (Violation of these warnings resulted in the one fatality.) Concerned parents' groups want Shooting Stars removed from store shelves now before any more injuries or deaths occur.

1. _____
   _____

2. The beef being sold in your neighborhood supermarket looks too fatty to be Choice, as labeled. You think the meat's true grade is only Good.

2. _____
   _____

3. You open a can of sliced peaches and empty its contents into a strainer to drain. The last thing out of the can is a dark, jagged strip of what proves to be metal. You are horrified. You discard the fruit but save the piece of metal and the can with its batch number. You think someone should investigate any food processor who allows such contamination.

3. _____
   _____

4. You are allergic to lanolin. When your hands, neck, and scalp break out in a rash, all evidence points to a new hair rinse as the culprit. You reread the label: no lanolin. You are sure it must be there, though. You have all the symptoms. You want the contents checked scientifically.

4. _____
   _____

5. A year ago, your aunt and uncle bought $15,000 of stock in a company that made security devices (smoke detectors, burglar alarms, electric gates). At the time it seemed like a good investment. The security business was booming, and the literature put out by the company looked impressive. Now, however, the company is bankrupt. (Its literature had seriously understated its debt and overstated its income.) Your relatives feel they were misled.

5. _____
   _____

6. Your cousin ordered a body-building kit he read about in a magazine ad. The ad stated that users of the kit could double or triple their strength in record time and supported this claim with photographs of an adult body builder. Your cousin paid $80 for the kit, which consisted of a series of booklets describing an exercise program, several cans of a dietary supplement, and a weight-lifting belt. He's been using these items for six months with nothing like the results pictured in the ad and feels gypped.

6. _____
   _____

7. The contents label of your new suit says 80 percent wool, but you don't believe it. The fabric wrinkles too easily, and the jacket is losing its shape after only three wearings.

7. _____
   _____

CHAPTER 2 Our Market System

REVIEWING CONSUMER TERMS

Using the terms below, write a paragraph about our market system.

economic system
market
economists
resources
productivity

recession
depression
inflation
Gross Domestic Product
balance of trade

_____

_____

_____

_____

_____

_____

_____

_____

_____

_____

_____

_____

_____

_____

_____

_____

_____

_____

_____

_____

_____

_____

_____

_____

_____

CHAPTER **2** *Our Market System*

REVIEWING FACTS AND IDEAS

1. What four questions must each economic system answer?

   _____

   _____

   _____

   _____

   _____

2. What countries use the traditional system, the command or controlled system, the capitalist or market system, and the mixed system?

   _____

   _____

   _____

   _____

   _____

   _____

3. What role does government play in the American economy?

   _____

   _____

   _____

   _____

   _____

4. When did the United States have a recession and a depression?

   _____

   _____

   _____

   _____

   _____

5. What does the Gross Domestic Product measure?

   _____

   _____

   _____

   _____

   _____

CHAPTER 2 *Our Market System*

APPLICATION ACTIVITY 1

Read the biographical sketches below. Then answer the questions that follow.

FORD, Henry (1863–1947), automotive pioneer and industrialist. Henry Ford was born in Dearborn, Michigan. Mechanically inclined from an early age, he left his father's farm to work as a machinist's apprentice in Detroit. After completing his training, he briefly repaired and operated steam engines. Then in 1891 he was hired as an engineer by the Edison Illuminating Company. In his spare time, he worked with friends to design and build a so-called horseless carriage.

Starting in 1899, Ford associated himself with a number of automotive ventures. One, the Detroit Automobile Company, failed. The second, the Henry Ford Company, was later reorganized as the Cadillac Motor Company. The third became the Ford Motor Company. Ford's contribution to the new firm was a car he and another young mechanic had developed. For it, he received 25½ percent of the company's stock.

Ford, however, wanted to do more than just produce good cars. He wanted to produce affordable ones. His devotion to this idea soon caused a rift with some of his backers. In 1907, in a dispute over this issue, he bought out the firm's principal shareholder. The next year the Model T appeared. Within five years, it became the first car to be produced by assembly-line methods.

In 1913 nearly a quarter of a million Model T's were produced. This enormous volume allowed Ford to sell the car for a mere $500. Suddenly the automobile was within the reach of the average person.

FIRESTONE, Harvey (1868–1938), inventor and rubber manufacturer. Harvey Firestone spent a lifetime involved with vehicles of one kind or another. As a young man, for example, he sold buggies in Detroit. Later he marketed carriage tires in Chicago.

Firestone founded the Firestone Company in Akron, Ohio, in 1900. Through it, he pioneered in the development and manufacture of a variety of rubber products including pneumatic tires for cars and trucks, tractor tires, and nonskid tire treads. His firm supplied all of the tires for Ford's Model T automobiles.

From the start, obtaining raw materials for his manufacturing operations was a special problem for Firestone. Southeast Asian growers had a monopoly on rubber and set prices accordingly. To break their control, Firestone set up rubber plantations in Africa, specifically in Liberia. By 1937 his firm was supplying fully one-fourth of all rubber used in the United States. The Asian monopoly had been broken.

WARD, Montgomery (1844–1913), merchandiser. Montgomery Ward began his career in 1859 when he was hired as a clerk by a general store in St. Joseph, Missouri. Later Ward became a traveling salesman, working primarily in rural areas. It was this experience that gave him the idea on which he would found a retailing empire.

During his travels, Ward became aware of the peculiar dilemma faced by farmers: they received relatively low wholesale prices for the crops they grew but had to buy things at relatively high retail prices. Ward's idea was to eliminate all the middlemen whose markups created this price difference. He would buy goods and sell them directly to farmers, adding only one low markup.

To keep his own costs down, Ward created a whole new kind of merchandising—mail order. In 1872 Montgomery Ward & Company issued its first catalog, a single printed sheet containing 150 items. Three years later, the company announced the first money back guarantee of customer satisfaction. A dozen years after that, annual sales passed the $1 million mark.

1. What vocabulary term used in Chapter 2 describes all three men?

   _____

2. List two major achievements that can be identified with each man.

   a. Ford: _____

   _____

   _____

   b. Firestone: _____

   _____

   _____

   c. Ward: _____

   _____

3. Each of the industrialists discussed lowered the price of the goods or services his firm produced so that they could be made available to a mass market. How did each man achieve these economies?

   a. Ford: _____

   _____

   b. Firestone: _____

   _____

   c. Ward: _____

   _____

4. Complete the time line. Below the scale, draw in bars representing each industrialist's lifetime.

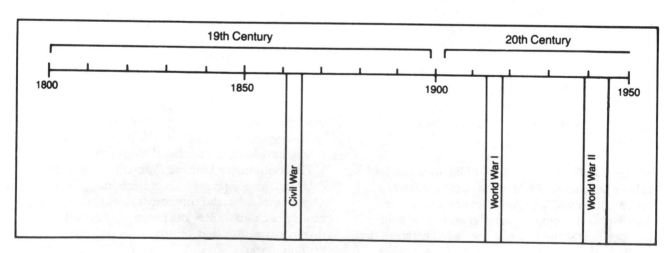

   a. According to the time line, which man lived the longest?   a. _____

   b. What key chronological landmark did all three men live through?   b. _____

   c. What key historical event did Ford live through that the other   _____
      industrialists did not?

                                                                      c. _____

   d. Which man died just before World War II broke out?   d. _____

CHAPTER **2** *Our Market System*

APPLICATION ACTIVITY 2

A. Assume you are the owner/operator of a small business called Torn T-Shirts, Inc. You buy bolts of cotton knit cloth. Two of your employees cut the cloth to pattern, and three others do the actual sewing. A sixth person irons on decals and does all necessary clerical work. How would you adjust to the following circumstances? In each case list your options and explain the effect on price.

1. Demand for T-shirts skyrockets. You can sell twice what you produce.

_____

_____

_____

_____

_____

2. The price of cotton cloth doubles.

_____

_____

_____

_____

_____

3. Quality control problems require that you replace your stitchers with more experienced people. You must pay these new employees 30 percent more.

_____

_____

_____

_____

_____

4. Demand for T-shirts slumps. You can sell only half of what you produce.

_____

_____

_____

_____

5. Demand for decaled T-shirts virtually disappears.

_____

_____

_____

_____

B. Complete the crossword puzzle by using vocabulary words and economic terms from Chapter 2.

ACROSS

1. _____-push inflation
4. Money owed, whether by a nation or an individual
8. _____ capita
10. State of being out of work
11. An excess of these results in a trade deficit
12. A nation's total output (abbrev.)
13. Economic slowdowns
16. Results when production costs exceed price
17. Payments to labor
18. Why people go into business in a free enterprise system: to make a _____

DOWN

1. Money used to buy factory equipment
2. Law of _____ and demand
3. Landlord's earnings
5. Relationship of imports and exports: _____ of trade
6. Opposite of foreign
7. Money paid for the use of money
8. How consumers shape our economy: through their _____
9. Land, labor, etc.
14. Often cited measure of inflation (abbrev.)
15. A manager's skills: entrepreneur _____

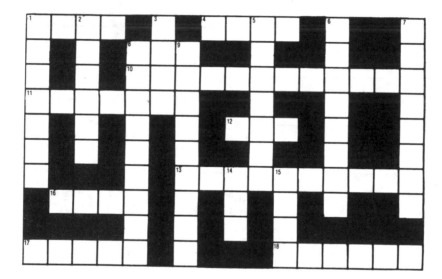

CHAPTER 3 *Government's Role*

REVIEWING CONSUMER TERMS

Incorporate all the terms below into a 250-word essay explaining the government's role.

disability benefits

excise taxes

monopoly

pension

progressive tax

proportional tax

real property

regressive tax

tariffs

taxable income

_____

_____

_____

_____

_____

_____

_____

_____

_____

_____

_____

_____

_____

_____

_____

_____

_____

_____

_____

_____

_____

_____

_____

_____

_____

CHAPTER **3** *Government's Role*

REVIEWING FACTS AND IDEAS

1. Name the three types of activities that government performs.

_____

2. List five common public services that government provides for citizens.

_____

_____

_____

3. Why do governments collect taxes?

_____

4. What is the difference between a direct and an indirect tax?

_____

_____

5. Identify various types of taxes.

_____

6. Describe how spending at the national level differs from government spending at the state and local levels.

_____

_____

_____

7. Summarize recent trends in tax reform.

_____

_____

8. List and explain five common taxes that you have paid or might pay in the near future.

_____

_____

_____

_____

_____

9. What are the steps you would follow in filling out and filing your tax return?

_____

_____

_____

CHAPTER 3 Government's Role

APPLICATION ACTIVITY 1

A. The Federal government spends billions of dollars each year on dozens of different programs. Fifteen such programs or possibilities are listed below in alphabetical order. Study them, then answer the questions that follow.

_____ Aid to the handicapped

_____ Conservation and wildlife preservation

_____ Consumer protection

_____ Development of alternate energy sources

_____ Economic aid to cities

_____ Educational loans (individuals) and grants (school systems)

_____ Funding for libraries and museums

_____ Government jobs for the unemployed

_____ Guaranteed national income

_____ Mass transit

_____ National defense

_____ Health insurance for the elderly

_____ Social security payment increases for the elderly

_____ Subsidies to business

_____ Welfare payment increases

1. Assume that you have the power to determine federal spending priorities. Which program would you rank first? Second? Continue numbering the items through fifteen.

_____

2. Check the accuracy of your list. Assume you have to reduce spending by one-third. Rather than cut across the board, you decide to eliminate funding for five programs.

   a. Which five?

   _____   _____   _____

   _____   _____   _____

   b. Where did these programs fall in your lists?

   _____

   Note: If any of the programs you choose to eliminate fell in the first half of your list, go back and reanalyze your priorities. Then renumber.

3. Assume that to reduce the federal deficit, you have to cut spending by yet another third. You can either eliminate three more programs or cut all ten by the same amount. Which would you choose to do and why? (Note: If you choose to cut programs, be sure to name them.)

   _____

   _____

   _____

   _____

   _____

   _____

   _____

   _____

B. Below are three documents that show tax payments the average consumer must make. Study the documents carefully.

PROPERTY LOCATION AND/OR PROPERTY DESCRIPTION

4444 TREASURY WAY   SOUTH WHIT
TRACT #201 N 25 FT OF LOT 6 AND ALL OF LOT 5

LOCALLY ASSESSED VALUES IN THIS COUNTY ARE DETERMINED BY THE LOS ANGELES COUNTY ASSESSOR
AT FULL VALUE EXCEPT AS OTHERWISE PROVIDED BY LAW.

	ASSESSED VALUE	EXEMPT TYPE	EXEMPTION VALUE	NET ASSESSED VALUE
1 LAND	33175			
2 IMPROVEMENTS	31556			
3 FIXTURES				
4				
5 TOTAL REAL PROPERTY	64731	HOME	7000	57731
6				
7				

ASSESSED VALUE OF REAL PROPERTY   64731
HOMEOWNER'S EXEMPTION ....
TOTAL APPLICABLE TAX RATE..............   1.089893
GROSS TAXES BEFORE APPLICATION OF HOMEOWNER'S TAX   705.48
TAX REDUCTION ATTRIBUTABLE TO STATE-FINANCED HOMEOWNER'S TAX
RELIEF PROGRAM***SEE PARAGRAPH NO. 3 ON REVERSE SIDE
TOTAL TAX AFTER ALLOWANCE FOR HOMEOWNER'S EXEMPTION 705.48
PERSONAL PROPERTY, DIRECT ASSESSMENT OR SPECIFIC LAND LEVY...   21.22
TOTAL TAXES DUE 726.70

A. _____ tax(es)

1 Control number 294200		OMB No. 1545-0008		
2 Employer's name, address, and ZIP code Greenfield Solar, Inc. 314 Lamont Street Van Nuys, CA 91405			3 Employer's identification number 11-222-33	4 Employer's state I.D. number 19-9/C
			5 Statutory employee / Deceased / Pension plan / Legal rep. / 942 emp. / Subtotal / Deferred compensation / Void	
			6 Allocated tips	7 Advance EIC payment
8 Employee's social security number 000-00-0000	9 Federal income tax withheld 1409.17		10 Wages, tips, other compensation 9033.16	11 Social security tax withheld 691.04
12 Employee's name, address, and ZIP code Albert Ian Pitkin 19425 Calle del Mar Santa Monica, CA 90402			13 Social security wages 9033.16	14 Social security tips
			16	16a Fringe benefits incl. in Box 10
			17 State income tax 406.49	18 State wages, tips, etc. 9033.16	19 Name of state CA
			20 Local income tax	21 Local wages, tips, etc.	22 Name of locality

Form W-2 Wage and Tax Statement
This information is being furnished to the Internal Revenue Service.
Copy B To be filed with employee's FEDERAL tax return   Dept. of the Treasury—IRS

C. _____ tax(es)

```
PEPREL'S
Linen Supply
3303 Tracee Blvd.
Philadelphia, PA 19136

1/23  2PM  CASH/TAKE
055  26  2929  61616


COMFTR 1          34.99
         TX        2.10
         TL       37.09
         PD       40.00
         CHG       2.91


Thank you for shopping
        PEPREL'S
```

B. _____ tax(es)

A. _____ tax(es)

B. _____ tax(es)

C. _____ tax(es)

1. Label each document with the specific tax (or taxes) it represents. Then circle those entries that show the amount of tax due or withheld.

2. What is the tax rate in each case? A. _____ %   B. _____ %   C. (FICA) _____ %

3. Refer to document B.

   a. Who is paying the tax? _____

   b. Who is collecting the tax? _____

   c. Who ultimately receives the tax money? _____

   d. Together these facts make B an example of a(n) _____ tax.

4. Refer to document C. Items 9 and 11 show funds withheld.

   a. Who is holding them? _____

   b. Till when? _____

   c. From whom are they being withheld? _____

   d. These facts make C an example of a(n) _____ tax.

CHAPTER 3 Government's Role

APPLICATION ACTIVITY 2

A. Compare the charts. Then answer the questions that follow.

THE FEDERAL GOVERNMENT DOLLAR: WHERE IT CAME FROM

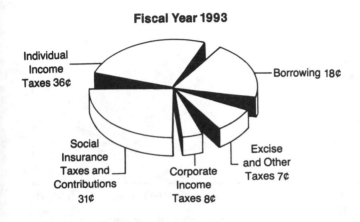

Fiscal Year 1993

Individual Income Taxes 36¢

Borrowing 18¢

Social Insurance Taxes and Contributions 31¢

Corporate Income Taxes 8¢

Excise and Other Taxes 7¢

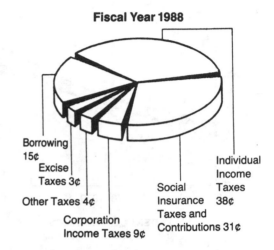

Fiscal Year 1988

Borrowing 15¢

Excise Taxes 3¢

Other Taxes 4¢

Corporation Income Taxes 9¢

Social Insurance Taxes and Contributions 31¢

Individual Income Taxes 38¢

1. Over the five-year period represented by the pie charts, what has happened to the following taxes as sources of federal revenue?

   a. Individual income taxes

   _____

   b. Corporate income taxes

   _____

   c. Social security taxes and contributions

   _____

   d. Excise and other taxes

   _____

2. Over the same period, what has happened to borrowing as a source of federal funds?

   _____

3. a. Based on the above answers, describe recent trends in financing the federal government.

   _____

   _____

   b. What reasons could account for these trends?

   _____

   c. Do you think these trends are healthy? Why or why not?

   _____

   _____

B. The graph below summarizes U.S. government spending for the twenty-year period from 1975 to 1994. Study the graph carefully. Then use the questions that follow to analyze its content.

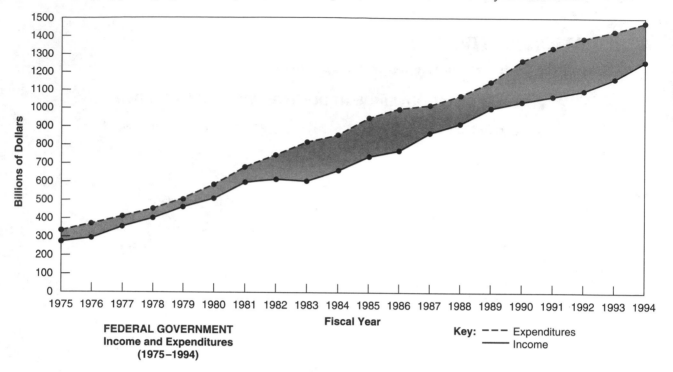

**FEDERAL GOVERNMENT
Income and Expenditures
(1975–1994)**

Key: ‒ ‒ ‒ Expenditures
——— Income

1. Describe the trend in government spending over the twenty years covered by the graph.

   _____

   _____

2. Wages are the worker's income. What is income to the government?

   _____

3. What trend did government income follow from 1975 to 1994?

   _____

   _____

4. a. In general, over the period of the graph has the government taken in more or less than it has spent?

   _____

   b. What does the shaded area of the graph represent?

   _____

   c. In which years did the shaded protion of the graph grow most rapidly? Why?

   _____

Chapter 4   *Global Economics*

REVIEWING CONSUMER TERMS

Use each of the following terms in a paragraph to demonstrate you know its meaning.

currency	international trade
embargo	protectionism
export	quota
free trade	telecommunications
import	trade deficit

CHAPTER 4 *Global Economics*

REVIEWING FACTS AND IDEAS

1. Give two reasons for countries to trade with one another.

   _____
   _____
   _____
   _____
   _____
   _____

2. How do consumers benefit from international trade? How are they harmed?

   _____
   _____
   _____
   _____
   _____
   _____

3. List the three major barriers to trade.

   _____
   _____
   _____
   _____
   _____

4. Why is international finance important?

   _____
   _____
   _____
   _____
   _____
   _____

CHAPTER 4 Global Economics

APPLICATION ACTIVITY 1

A. The table below shows exports by U.S. businesses to some of the country's major trading partners. The amounts are in millions of dollars. Look at the table and then answer the questions that follow.

U.S. Exports: 1990 to 1994
(In Millions of Dollars)

Country	1990	1991	1992	1993	1994
Canada	83,674	85,150	90,594	100,444	114,441
China	4,806	6,278	7,418	8,763	9,287
Germany	18,760	21,302	21,302	18,932	19,237
Japan	48,580	48,125	47,813	47,892	53,481
Mexico	28,279	33,277	40,592	41,581	50,840
United Kingdom	23,490	22,046	22,800	26,438	26,833

Source: Statistical Abstract of the United States, 1995.

1. Which country is the largest recipient of U.S. exports?

   _____

2. Which country had the largest dollar growth in exports over the five-year period? By what amount?

   _____

   _____

3. Which country had the largest percentage growth in exports over the five-year period? By what percentage?

   _____

4. Based on export dollars, which countries offer the best markets for U.S. products. Explain why you think this is the case.

   _____

   _____

   _____

   _____

   _____

   _____

   _____

   _____

   _____

   _____

   _____

B. The table below shows imports by the United States from several trading partners. The amounts are in millions of dollars. Look at the table and then answer the questions that follow.

U.S. Imports: 1990 to 1994
(In Millions of Dollars)

Country	1990	1991	1992	1993	1994
Canada	91,380	91,064	98,630	111,216	128,948
China	15,237	18,969	25,728	31,540	38,781
Germany	28,162	26,137	28,820	28,562	31,749
Japan	89,684	91,511	97,414	107,246	119,149
Mexico	30,157	31,130	35,211	39,917	49,493
United Kingdom	20,188	18,413	20,093	21,730	25,063

Source: Statistical Abstract of the United States, 1995.

1. From which country do we import the most? Why do you think this is the case?

_____

_____

_____

_____

_____

_____

2. From which country did we increase imports by the largest percentage over the five-year period? By what percentage?

_____

_____

_____

_____

3. As the import table shows, the United States is a very large market for goods from other countries. Explain why you think the U.S. is such a good market for other countries.

_____

_____

_____

_____

_____

_____

_____

_____

_____

CHAPTER 4 *Global Economics*

APPLICATION ACTIVITY 2

A. The United States sells some products to countries and buys other products from that same country. The difference between the total amount of sales and the total amount of purchases is called the balance of trade. Determine the balance of trade with each country listed below by subtracting imports from exports. If imports are larger than exports, use a minus sign to show the negative number.

	Exports	Imports	Balance
Canada	114,441	128,216	_____
China	9,287	38,781	_____
Germany	19,237	31,749	_____
Japan	53,481	119,149	_____
Mexico	50,840	49,493	_____
United Kingdom	26,833	25,063	_____

1. With which countries does the United States have a positive balance of trade (buys less from a country than it spends on goods from that country).

   _____

   _____

2. With which countries does the United States have a negative balance of trade?

   _____

   _____

3. With which country is the negative balance of trade the largest? Why do you think this is so?

   _____

   _____

   _____

   _____

   _____

4. Why are the balance of trade figures important to a country?

   _____

   _____

   _____

   _____

   _____

   _____

   _____

   _____

B. Without imports, people in the United States would have to do without some products that are not grown or made here. For example, coffee is not grown in the United States. People in other countries also rely on the United States to provide them with products that they would not otherwise have, such as some agricultural products. Look at the items below and decide whether each is exported or imported by the U.S. You may need to do some research to find the answers.

Coffee Beans

Tea Leaves

Pepper

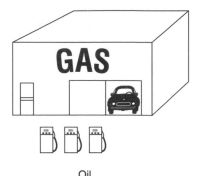
Oil

Cotton

Wheat

Machinery

1. Which of the items shown above are imported by the United States? Why?

_____

_____

_____

_____

2. Which items are exported to other countries? Why?

_____

_____

_____

_____

3. If we could no longer import items such as these, what changes would we have to make to accommodate the lack of these products?

_____

_____

_____

_____

Unit 1 Lab You in the Economy

STUDYING THE MARKET SYSTEM'S EFFECT ON WORKERS, CONSUMERS, AND CITIZENS

Unit 1 discusses the major economic roles that most American adults fulfill in the U.S. market system. In this lab, you will explore the system's effect on workers, consumers, and citizens.

TOOLS

1. Financial magazines
2. Newspapers
3. Television and radio news stories
4. Literature from government agencies and elected representatives

PROCEDURES

Read the lab in your textbook and complete each activity using the space provided below.

Step A

Expert's name: _____

Telephone number: _____

Step B

Public service consultant #1: _____

Telephone number: _____

Address: _____

Public service consultant #2: _____

Telephone number: _____

Address: _____

Step C

Employee #1: _____

Telephone number: _____

Address: _____

Employee #2: _____

Telephone number: _____

Address: _____

LAB REPORT
Step D

Use your research and your notes from the five interviews to answer the questions below.

1. What is the current sales tax rate in your area?

   _____

   _____

2. If a consumer bought a refrigerator for $459, what would the sales tax on the purchase be?

   _____

   _____

3. What is the property tax rate for a home in your area?

   _____

4. If a home's assessed value is $159,000, what would the home owners pay annually in property taxes?

   _____

   _____

Step E

Using a word processor or typewriter, write a two-page report explaining how the business cycle and taxation rates affect workers, consumers, and citizens.

UNIT 2 Money Management: Earning and Spending

ATTITUDE INVENTORY

Before you begin Unit 2, take stock of your attitudes by completing the following inventory. Read each statement and decide how you feel about it—agree, disagree, or undecided. Write your answers in the blanks.

1. The best way to get a job is to let an employment agency find one.

2. A good time to plan for a career is while you are in college.

3. A person's standard of living depends largely on his or her choice of career.

4. A person who has an uncertain income has a good excuse for not budgeting.

5. The family budget should be the sole responsibility of one person.

6. If you can keep track of spending in your head, you do not need to use a budget.

7. Once a budget has been drawn up, it should not be changed.

8. As long as you live within your income, there is no need to keep a budget or expense record.

9. Most product advertising contains too much exaggeration and misinformation to be helpful.

10. A salesperson who tries to interest you in a more expensive item is just doing his or her job.

11. It is illegal to print or broadcast advertisements that mislead consumers.

12. You cannot trust a salesperson to tell you the truth.

13. A pyramid scheme or chain letter could make you rich.

14. The best way to resolve a consumer complaint is to write a letter to the president of the company.

15. Resolving a consumer complaint in court is expensive because it requires the services of an attorney.

1. _____

2. _____

3. _____

4. _____

5. _____

6. _____

7. _____

8. _____

9. _____

10. _____

11. _____

12. _____

13. _____

14. _____

15. _____

RECHECKING YOUR ATTITUDE

Before going on to the next unit, answer the Attitude Inventory questions a second time. Then compare the two sets of responses. On how many statements have your attitudes changed? Can you account for these shifts in your opinions? What do you know now that you did not know then?

1. The best way to get a job is to let an employment agency find one.

1. _____

2. A good time to plan for a career is while you are in college.

2. _____

3. A person's standard of living depends largely on his or her choice of career.

3. _____

4. A person who has an uncertain income has a good excuse for not budgeting.

4. _____

5. The family budget should be the sole responsibility of one person.

5. _____

6. If you can keep track of spending in your head, you do not need to use a budget.

6. _____

7. Once a budget has been drawn up, it should not be changed.

7. _____

8. As long as you live within your income, there is no need to keep a budget or expense record.

8. _____

9. Most product advertising contains too much exaggeration and misinformation to be helpful.

9. _____

10. A salesperson who tries to interest you in a more expensive item is just doing his or her job.

10. _____

11. It is illegal to print or broadcast advertisements that mislead consumers.

11. _____

12. You cannot trust a salesperson to tell you the truth.

12. _____

13. A pyramid scheme or chain letter could make you rich.

13. _____

14. The best way to resolve a consumer complaint is to write a letter to the president of the company.

14. _____

15. Resolving a consumer complaint in court is expensive because it requires the services of an attorney.

15. _____

Answers changed _____ Why? _____

_____

_____

_____

_____

_____

_____

_____

_____

_____

_____

_____

CHAPTER 5 Choosing a Career

REVIEWING CONSUMER TERMS

In a paragraph, define the term *entrepreneurship* and then explain the relationship of the following terms to it.

abilities   needs
apprenticeship program   résumé
aptitudes   standard of living
entrepreneur   wants

_____

_____

_____

_____

_____

_____

_____

_____

_____

_____

_____

_____

_____

_____

_____

_____

_____

_____

_____

_____

_____

_____

_____

_____

_____

_____

_____

_____

_____

_____

CHAPTER 5 *Choosing a Career*

REVIEWING FACTS AND IDEAS

1. What qualities should you know about yourself in order to make a good career choice?

   _____

   _____

   _____

   _____

2. What references should be used to research a career?

   _____

   _____

   _____

   _____

   _____

3. List the steps you would take to prepare for an interview.

   _____

   _____

   _____

   _____

   _____

4. Name some effective job search techniques.

   _____

   _____

   _____

5. What laws protect you as an employee?

   _____

   _____

   _____

6. What are some of the advantages and some disadvantages of being an entrepreneur?

   _____

   _____

   _____

   _____

CHAPTER **5** *Choosing a Career*

APPLICATION ACTIVITY 1

Below are some excerpts from the 1995 edition of the Occupational Outlook Handbook. Read them carefully. Then answer the questions on the next page.

Architects

Nature of the Work Architects design buildings using paper and pencil, as well as computer-aided design and drafting (CADD) technology. They may also advise on the selection of building sites and prepare land use and environmental impact studies.

Training Licensed architects must meet three requirements: A professional degree in architecture (generally 5 years of study), a period of practical training or internship (usually 3 years), and passage of all sections of the Architect Registration Examination.

Job Outlook Although employment is expected to rise as fast as the average for all occupations through 2005, architects may still face competition, particularly for jobs in the most prestigious firms with the best opportunities for advancement. Employment opportunities are highly dependent on level of local construction, which is cyclical. During recessions, architects will face strong competition for jobs and clients.

Earnings The median salary for intern-architects was $24,500 in 1992; for licensed architects with 8–10 years experience, $36,700; for managers or partners in a firm, $50,000 (some in large practices earned over $100,000).

Dietitians

Nature of the Work Dietitians plan nutrition programs, supervise the preparation and serving of meals for institutions, and promote sound eating habits.

Training The basic educational requirement is a bachelor's degree with a major in dietetics, foods and nutrition, food service systems management or related area. Thirty states have laws governing dietetics. The American Dietetic Association (ADA) awards the Registered Dietitian credential to those

who pass a certification exam after completing their academic education and supervised experience. The experience can be received in a 4-year program or during an internship of 9-12 months.

Job Outlook Employment of dietitians is expected to grow as fast as the average for all occupations through the year 2005 as demand grows for meals and nutritional counseling in nursing homes . . . community health programs and home health care agencies.

Earnings The average minimum salary in 1992 was $25,122; those with 6–10 years of experience had a median annual income of $32,900 in 1991. The average maximum salary in 1992 was $37,467.

Medical Records Technicians

Nature of the Work Medical records technicians organize and evaluate patients' medical records for completeness and accuracy. They also tabulate and analyze data to help improve patient care, control costs, and to respond to surveys or legal actions.

Training Usually formal training is required in a 2-year associate degree program offered at community and junior colleges.

Job Outlook Employment is expected to grow much faster than the average for all occupations through the year 2005 due to rapid growth in the number of medical tests, treatments and procedures, and because medical records will be increasingly scrutinized by third-party payers, courts, and consumers.

Earnings The average annual salary for medical records technicians in the federal government in nonsupervisory, supervisory, and managerial positions was $22,008 in 1993. The average salary in 1992 for accredited record technicians in supervisory positions averaged $29,599 per year.

1. Which job requires the most formal education?

_____

2. Which job pays the best?

_____

3. What relationship, if any, seems to exist between education and salary?

_____

_____

_____

_____

_____

4. Which job category offers the best prospects for employment? Why?

_____

_____

_____

_____

_____

_____

_____

_____

5. Which job category is the most competitive? Why?

_____

_____

_____

_____

_____

_____

_____

_____

_____

_____

_____

_____

_____

_____

_____

_____

CHAPTER 5   *Choosing a Career*

APPLICATION ACTIVITY 2

Sally Fenwick is interested in answering the classified ad at the right. Sally wants to become an executive assistant, and so for the next two years she will be taking an administrative assistant program at the local community college. She needs a part-time job to help with expenses.

For the past two summers, Sally has worked as a receptionist and a data-entry clerk, respectively. She has a business diploma from James Madison High School, where she maintained a B average. Her special skills include word processing (using Microsoft Word and WordPerfect) at a speed of 65 wpm, and operating copiers and fax machines. Sally has been active in student government, serving as a junior class representative to the student council and senior class treasurer. Use this information to draft a résumé for Sally. Write out the document by hand using the space on the next page and following the model resume below.

> **WORD PROCESSOR**
> Growing cable TV firm seeks part-time word processor for afternoons and weekends (20 hrs./wk.). Need excellent word processing skills (60 wpm with good proofreading ability). Send resume to DAILY TIMES Box 411.

JOHN FRANKLIN
1345 Delaware Street
Chicago, Illinois 60611
(312) 555-1234

OBJECTIVES:	Immediate: Word Processing Trainee Long-range: Word Processing Manager
EXPERIENCE:	
Summer 1996	Social Security Administration, Chicago, Illinois Junior Clerk-Typist
1995-1996	First Federal National Bank, Chicago, Illinois Office Co-op Clerical Intern (part-time), Word Processing Center
1993-1995	Sun Times, Inc., Chicago, Illinois Deliveryperson
SKILLS:	Keyboarding (50 wpm) Proficient in WordPerfect Proficient with office machines such as fax and copiers
EDUCATION:	Miller Senior High, Chicago, Illinois Grade Average: B+
ACTIVITIES:	President, Future Business Leaders of America Club Treasurer, Youth Block Club Member, National Honor Society
REFERENCES:	Available on request.

Use this space to write the resume for Sally Fenwick.

CHAPTER **6** *Budgeting Your Money*

REVIEWING CONSUMER TERMS

Use each of the following terms in a sentence that demonstrates you know its meaning.

assets
average annual expenditures
balance sheet
budget
emergency fund

fixed expenses
flexible expenses
liabilities
net worth
net income

_____

_____

_____

_____

_____

_____

_____

_____

_____

_____

_____

_____

_____

_____

_____

_____

_____

_____

_____

_____

_____

_____

_____

_____

CHAPTER 6 Budgeting Your Money

REVIEWING FACTS AND IDEAS

1. What are the five steps in planning a budget?

_____

_____

_____

_____

2. List the common methods of recordkeeping.

_____

_____

_____

_____

_____

3. What are the three most common mistakes consumers make when budgeting?

_____

_____

_____

_____

_____

4. When should consumers revise their budgets?

_____

_____

_____

_____

5. What information does a balance sheet show?

_____

_____

_____

_____

_____

CHAPTER **6** *Budgeting Your Money*

APPLICATION ACTIVITY 1

Josh takes home $1,155 a month. He has the following estimated expenses for March.

Car payment.	$150	Glasses (new prescription).	$150
Church donations	20	Groceries	100
Dad's birthday	30	Meals out	100
Dry-cleaning	20	Rent	200
Entertainment	100	Savings (50 percent to emergency fund).	150
Gas (car)	75	Telephone	25
Gas and electricity (apt.)	25	Subscriptions.	10

1. Does Josh have enough income to cover his expenses? To find out, complete the personal budget form provided below.

INCOME, EXPENSES, AND SAVINGS	AMOUNT FOR
Total income	_____
Savings:	
Emergency fund	_____
Savings account..	_____
Fixed expenses:	
Rent or mortgage payment .... _____	
Installment payments (car) .... _____	
Other .... _____	
Total .... _____	_____
Flexible expenses:	
Food .... _____	
Utilities .... _____	
Household supplies and furnishings.................. _____	
Clothing .... _____	
Transportation (gas and maintenance) .... _____	
Misc. health care products and services.............. _____	
Entertainment .... _____	
Personal .... _____	
Gifts and contributions .... _____	
Total .... _____	_____
Total savings and expenses....................................	_____

2. What percentage of his take-home pay is Josh spending on each of the following items? Show your computations.

    a. Food _____

    b. Rent (including utilities) _____

    c. Transportation _____

    d. Medical expenses _____

    e. Savings _____

    f. Entertainment _____

3. How does Josh's take-home pay and monthly expenditures compare with those shown for one person in the average annual expenditure chart in your textbook? What might cause differences?

_____

_____

_____

_____

4. Because of a shortage of parts, the plant where Josh works will be shut down for five days in April. As a result, Josh's monthly take-home pay will be reduced to $860. Josh is not sure he can make ends meet in the face of such a drastic salary reduction. Using March's expenses as a starting point, do a second budget for Josh and show him how he can manage.

INCOME, EXPENSES, AND SAVINGS		AMOUNT FOR
Total income..		_____
Savings:		
Emergency fund		_____
Savings account..		_____
Fixed expenses:		
Rent or mortgage payment	_____	
Installment payments (car)	_____	
Other	_____	
Total	_____	_____
Flexible expenses:		
Food	_____	
Utilities	_____	
Household supplies and furnishings.................	_____	
Clothing	_____	
Transportation (gas and maintenance)	_____	
Misc. health care products and services..............	_____	
Entertainment..	_____	
Personal	_____	
Gifts and contributions	_____	
Total	_____	_____
Total savings and expenses		_____

5. a. In which expense category did you make most of your cuts? Check one:

_____Savings _____Fixed expenses _____Flexible expenses

b. In which specific areas will Josh have to make a special effort to control his spending?

_____

c. Give Josh some specific hints for holding down expenses in the checked categories.

_____

_____

_____

_____

CHAPTER **6** *Budgeting Your Money*

APPLICATION ACTIVITY 2

Carmen has just finished her fourth year as a teacher. She rooms with another teacher in an apartment complex near the school. Her cash balance in her checking account is usually $500. She has $2,000 in a savings account for emergencies. She also is saving for a trip to Europe, which she will combine with a college credit course to advance her position on the salary scale. So far, Carmen has put aside $1,500 for the trip. Equity in her pension plan is $12,000, and she has invested $2,000 in a mutual fund. Carmen owns a car worth $15,000, a stereo system with a value of about $400, miscellaneous clothing and jewelry worth about $900, and furniture worth about $900.

Carmen has an outstanding bill of $300 for a recent purchase of school clothes, and she owes $10,000 on her car. Using this information, prepare a balance sheet for Carmen on the form provided on the next page. Then answer the questions below.

1. What are Carmen's total assets? liabilities?

_____

_____

2. How did you arrive at a figure for Carmen's durable assets? her "other" assets?

_____

_____

_____

_____

_____

3. Which assets are long-term investments?

_____

_____

4. What is a plan Carmen might make to acquire other major assets?

_____

_____

_____

_____

5. What is Carmen's major liability?

_____

_____

6. What is Carmen's net worth? How did you determine it? How was she able to acquire this amount?

_____

_____

_____

_____

CONSUMER BALANCE SHEET

ASSETS:

Cash in checking accounts . . . . _____

Cash in savings accounts . . . . _____

Current value of government savings bonds . . . . _____

Cash surrender value of insurance policies . . . . _____

Equity in pensions . . . . _____

Current value of annuities . . . . _____

Current value of durable assets (car, house,
furnishings, and equipment) . . . . _____

Cash value of ownership of a business. . . . . _____

Value of investment real estate owned . . . . _____

Market value of securities _____

     Bonds . . . . _____

     Stocks . . . . _____

     Mutual funds. . . . . _____

     Investment trusts . . . . _____

Other assets _____

_____ _____

TOTAL . . . . _____

LIABILITIES:

Current bills outstanding . . . . _____

Amount owed on installment purchases . . . . _____

Amount owed on personal loans . . . . _____

Amount due on real estate mortgages . . . . _____

Amount due on taxes . . . .

Other liabilities

_____ _____

_____ _____

_____

TOTAL . . . . _____

NET WORTH . . . . _____

CHAPTER 7 *Spending Money Wisely*

REVIEWING CONSUMER TERMS

Use each of the following terms in a paragraph to demonstrate you know its meaning.

conspicuous consumption
cooperative
habit
impulse purchase
life stage

lifestyle
retail stores
sales promotions
status symbol
values

_____

_____

_____

_____

_____

_____

_____

_____

_____

_____

_____

_____

_____

_____

_____

_____

_____

_____

_____

_____

_____

_____

_____

_____

_____

_____

_____

_____

_____

_____

CHAPTER 7 *Spending Money Wisely*

REVIEWING FACTS AND IDEAS

1. How do personal, social, and business factors influence consumer spending? Provide one example of each.

_____

_____

_____

_____

_____

_____

2. What are the seven steps of decision making that should be applied to all major purchases?

_____

_____

_____

_____

_____

3. What are seven types of retail stores?

_____

_____

_____

_____

_____

_____

4. In what ways does when you buy affect how much you pay?

_____

_____

_____

_____

_____

_____

CHAPTER **7** *Spending Money Wisely*

APPLICATION ACTIVITY 1

You used to have a bike—a ten-speed racer you received as a hand-me-down from your cousin. You used the bike for school and errands and occasional weekend cycling trips with friends. You used it until last month when your brother backed into it with the family car. The damage he did was not repairable.

A new bike with similar features will cost at least $300. That amount, while large, is not beyond your means. You have a part-time job and bring home about $75 a week. With that money, you pay for school lunches, recreational expenses, and all of your own clothing. (Note: During the summers, when you can work longer hours, you triple your take-home pay. Most of this extra money, however, goes into your bank account for college. Later this year you plan to apply to the state university, where you would like to major in commercial art.)

There is one other set of factors you must consider before committing yourself to any large purchase. Your cousin is getting married early next month. For the wedding you will need to buy dress shoes. This is no small matter. You must have special shoes, whose alteration adds about one-third to their cost. In addition, your parents will be giving your cousin a substantial wedding gift. You have to decide whether or not to contribute.

Should you buy a new bike? Use the seven-step procedure outlined in your text to examine your options and reach a decision.

1. Define the issue or problem.

   _____
   _____
   _____

2. Identify relevant values and goals.

   _____
   _____
   _____
   _____
   _____
   _____
   _____
   _____

3. List possible choices (even those that seem out of the ordinary).

   _____
   _____
   _____
   _____
   _____
   _____

4. Gather information.

_____

_____

_____

_____

_____

_____

5. Evaluate the choices.

_____

_____

_____

_____

_____

_____

_____

_____

_____

_____

6. Make a decision.

_____

_____

_____

_____

7. Evaluate the results.

_____

_____

_____

_____

_____

CHAPTER 7 Spending Money Wisely

APPLICATION ACTIVITY 2

Choose one item in each of the three categories listed (clothing, electronics, sports equipment) that you would like to purchase. Research quality, price, selection and service in four different types of stores that sell each of the items. Use a rating scale of 1-5, with 5 being best, to rate each store in each category. Then answer the questions on the next page.

Clothing item: _____

	Price	Quality	Selection	Service
Store A: _____	_____	_____	_____	_____
Store B: _____	_____	_____	_____	_____
Store C: _____	_____	_____	_____	_____
Store D: _____	_____	_____	_____	_____

Electronic item: _____

	Price	Quality	Selection	Service
Store A: _____	_____	_____	_____	_____
Store B: _____	_____	_____	_____	_____
Store C _____	_____	_____	_____	_____
Store D: _____	_____	_____	_____	_____

Sports equipment item: _____

	Price	Quality	Selection	Service
Store A: _____	_____	_____	_____	_____
Store B: _____	_____	_____	_____	_____
Store C: _____	_____	_____	_____	_____
Store D: _____	_____	_____	_____	_____

1. Which store(s)—A, B, C, or D—offered the best quality, price, service, and selection for each type of item?

Best Quality

Clothing _____

Electronics _____

Sporting equipment _____

Best Price

Clothing _____

Electronics _____

Sporting equipment _____

Best Service

Clothing _____

Electronics _____

Sporting equipment _____

Best Selection

Clothing _____

Electronics _____

Sporting equipment _____

2. a. Which type(s) of stores had the best quality?

_____

_____

b. Which type(s) of stores had the best prices?

_____

_____

c. Which type(s) of stores usually provided the best service?

_____

_____

d. Which type(s) of stores had the best selection?

_____

_____

3. How would you decide on the best type of store for the item you want to buy?

_____

_____

_____

_____

_____

_____

CHAPTER Consumer Problems and Their Solutions

REVIEWING CONSUMER TERMS

Use the following terms in a paragraph to demonstrate you know their meaning.

bait and switch
class-action suit
deception
fraud
loss leader

mediation
puffery
small-claims courts
trading up

_____

_____

_____

_____

_____

_____

_____

_____

_____

_____

_____

_____

_____

_____

_____

_____

_____

_____

_____

_____

_____

_____

_____

_____

_____

_____

_____

CHAPTER **8** Consumer Problems and Their Solutions

REVIEWING FACTS AND IDEAS

1. How is fraud different from deception?

_____

_____

_____

_____

_____

2. Give examples of two misleading advertising practices.

_____

_____

_____

_____

3. Why are bait-and-switch advertising, chain letters, and pyramid schemes fraudulent?

_____

_____

_____

_____

_____

_____

4. List the steps to follow in making a consumer complaint.

_____

_____

_____

_____

5. What is a small-claims court?

_____

_____

_____

_____

_____

CHAPTER 8 Consumer Problems and Their Solutions

APPLICATION ACTIVITY 1

Ads are often written in a way that encourages consumers to read more into them than is in fact there. Consider the following statements and phrases. In what ways, if any, are they misleading? Be careful to distinguish what is said from what is implied.

1. "A $79 value . . . Our price $39.95"

_____
_____
_____

2. "With Texarcron you get more miles per gallon."

_____
_____
_____

3. "Comes in Large Extra Large and Jumbo sizes"

_____
_____
_____

4. "Hair Repair will restore that baby-soft silkiness to your hair or your money back."

_____
_____
_____

5. "The honey made nature's way . . ."

_____
_____

6. "10% off our low everyday prices"

_____
_____

7. "Unbelievable savings on imported cameras!"

_____
_____

8. "Extra-strength Puff-Stuff has more softening power than two leading brands combined. "

_____
_____
_____

CHAPTER 8   Consumer Problems and Their Solutions

APPLICATION ACTIVITY 2

You have tried unsuccessfully to resolve a consumer complaint by contacting the company involved. In these circumstances, as a last resort, it is often a good idea to write to the president of the firm. For this kind of correspondence, you should be factual, organized, and brief. The form letter below can help you. Use it to write a complaint based on the following facts. (Create any details you need to make your letter realistic and convincing.)

Item: Hotspot-Kelby CD player. **Purchased:** Simm's Department Store, March 14. **Satisfactory use:** 1 month. **Problem:** CD tray fails to open. **Service record:** April 18—left at authorized service center; May 2—problem diagnosed as defective switch; May 16, 23—service center inquiries (part still not in); June 6—inquiry to Hotspot-Kelby consumer relations department (no response to date).

Use the space below to make notes about what you want to say in each part of the letter.

	_____
	_____
	Complainant's address
	_____
	Date
_____ , President	
_____	
_____	
Corporate address	
Dear	

(#1 purchase facts) _____

_____

(#2 problem details) _____

_____

_____

_____

_____

(#3 remedy sought) _____

_____

_____

_____

I trust that with your help this problem can be resolved satisfactorily. In that hope, I shall refrain from taking any further action for two weeks. If I do not hear from you or your company by then, however, I shall refer the matter to a government consumer agency for action.

Sincerely,

_____

Your signature

Enc.

UNIT 2 Lab Money Management: Earning and Spending

OBSERVING AN ENTREPRENEUR

Unit 2 discusses the earning and spending facets of money management and focuses on the many responsibilities of entrepreneurs. In this lab, you will make a further exploration into entrepreneurial opportunities and obligations.

TOOLS

1. Financial and business magazines
2. Literature from the Better Business Bureau and government offices
3. Consumer magazines
4. *Occupational Outlook Handbook* and other career references

PROCEDURES

Read the lab in your textbook and complete each activity using the space provided below.

Step A

Entrepreneur's name: _____

Telephone number: _____

Address: _____

Interview questions:

_____

_____

_____

_____

_____

_____

_____

_____

_____

_____

_____

_____

_____

_____

_____

_____

_____

_____

Step B
Date/time of appointment: _____

_____

_____

_____

_____

Lab Report
Step C

Use your observation and interview notes as well as the information in the textbook to answer the questions below.

1. If an employee's wage rate is $7 per hour and the employee receives 1.5 times the regular rate for every hour over 40 hours a week, how much will the employee earn for 51 hours worked in a week?

   _____

2. Herondo is a salesperson for a computer-hardware business. His salary is $1,000 a month and 5 percent of sales over $15,000. What was Herondo's salary for April, when he sold $33,000 worth of merchandise?

   _____

3. Eileen's Essentials is a stationery store that caters to the needs of small businesses. If Eileen had sales of $24,890 in June and expenses of $21,736 during the same month, what was the business's net income for June?

   _____

Step D

Using a word processor or a typewriter, write a two-page report explaining how a business's success is affected by financial management, employee policies, and customer-service issues.

UNIT 3 Money Management: Saving and Investing

ATTITUDE INVENTORY

Before you begin Unit 3, take stock of your attitudes by completing the following inventory. Read each statement and decide how you feel about it—agree, disagree, or undecided. Write your answers in the blanks.

1. Saving and investing money is possible only if you are rich.
   1. _____

2. A knowledge of saving and investment opportunities should be part of every person's basic education.
   2. _____

3. Every family should save at least 10 percent of its income.
   3. _____

4. With old-age assistance and social security available, people do not need long-range investment programs.
   4. _____

5. The only kind of bank account you really need is a checking account.
   5. _____

6. People should put their savings where they can get the highest return on their money, regardless of the risk involved.
   6. _____

7. A consumer should have a sizable emergency fund accumulated before buying stocks and bonds.
   7. _____

8. Saving only a small amount each week is not worthwhile.
   8. _____

9. A person is more likely to save when he or she has a definite goal in mind.
   9. _____

10. Having a check canceled reflects badly on the person who drew it.
    10. _____

11. You can take your money out of the bank anytime you wish—after all, it's your money!
    11. _____

12. There is no difference between investing and gambling.
    12. _____

13. An individual risks more by investing in corporate stocks than by putting money in a savings account.
    13. _____

RECHECKING YOUR ATTITUDE

Before going on to the next unit, answer the Attitude Inventory questions a second time. Then compare the two sets of responses. On how many statements have your attitudes changed? Can you account for these shifts in your opinions? What do you know now that you did not know then?

1. Saving and investing money is possible only if you are rich.   1. _____

2. A knowledge of saving and investment opportunities should be part of every person's basic education.   2. _____

3. Every family should save at least 10 percent of its income.   3. _____

4. With old-age assistance and social security available, people do not need long-range investment programs.   4. _____

5. The only kind of bank account you really need is a checking account.   5. _____

6. People should put their savings where they can get the highest return on their money, regardless of the risk involved.   6. _____

7. A consumer should have a sizable emergency fund accumulated before buying stocks and bonds.   7. _____

8. Saving only a small amount each week is not worthwhile.   8. _____

9. A person is more likely to save when he or she has a definite goal in mind.   9. _____

10. Having a check canceled reflects badly on the person who drew it.   10. _____

11. You can take your money out of the bank anytime you wish--after all, it's your money!   11. _____

12. There is no difference between investing and gambling.   12. _____

13. An individual risks more by investing in corporate stocks than by putting money in a savings account.   13. _____

Answers changed_____ Why?_____

_____

_____

_____

_____

_____

_____

_____

_____

_____

_____

_____

_____

_____

_____

_____

_____

CHAPTER  *Planning a Savings Program*

REVIEWING CONSUMER TERMS

For each group of terms, write a paragraph explaining what the listed items have to do with the heading.

Savings as Investment
investments
compounding

Savings Institutions

liquidity	dividend
annual percentage yield	savings and loan associations
commercial banks	credit union
mutual savings banks	

_____

_____

_____

_____

_____

_____

_____

_____

_____

_____

_____

_____

_____

_____

_____

_____

_____

_____

_____

_____

_____

_____

CHAPTER 9   *Planning a Savings Program*

REVIEWING FACTS AND IDEAS

1. What do you determine when you apply the rule of 72?

   _____

   _____

   _____

   _____

2. In general, what percent of income after taxes do or should consumers save?

   _____

   _____

   _____

   _____

   _____

3. What characteristic do most successful savers have in common?

   _____

   _____

   _____

   _____

4. What do credit unions pay out to their saving customers instead of interest?

   _____

   _____

   _____

5. Why might U.S. savings bonds be an attractive investment for many people?

   _____

   _____

   _____

   _____

CHAPTER  *Planning a Savings Program*

APPLICATION ACTIVITY 1

Saving is easier when there is a reason for it. The problems below explore some of the reasons young people have (or should have) for regularly depositing money in a savings account.

1. A poll was taken recently of teenage savers. It revealed that most save for some definite goal.

Goal	%
Education	30
Clothing	20
Automobile	12
Sports equipment	8
Photographic equipment	1
Stereo equipment/radio	1
Computer	1
No special goal	27

a. What percentage of teenagers surveyed had a definite reason for saving?

_____

b. What was the most common savings goal?

_____

c. What percentage of teenagers were saving for material goals?

_____

2. One reason for saving not apparently considered important by the young people surveyed was investment. Nonetheless, the compounding of interest can substantially increase even small amounts of money left on deposit. Consider the chart below.

COMPOUNDING OF $1				
Time	Compounded Annually		Compounded Semiannually	
	5-1/2%	6%	5-1/2%	6%
5 years	1.3073	1.3382	1.3102	1.3439
10 years	1.7099	1.7908	1.7224	1.8061
15 years	2.2377	2.3965	2.2625	2.4273

a. Craig's grandmother deposited $1,200 in a savings account for college five years ago. If the money has been in a bank that pays 5-1/2 percent interest compounded annually and there have been no withdrawals or further deposits, what is the present balance in the account?

_____

b. Suppose the bank had paid interest semiannually (twice a year). What would Craig's balance be?

_____

c. Suppose the bank had paid 6 percent interest compounded semiannually. How much would Craig have earned?

_____

d. Suppose you had a choice of two banks, one compounding interest quarterly and the other compounding it daily. Which would you choose and why?

_____

_____

_____

CHAPTER **9** *Planning a Savings Program*

APPLICATION ACTIVITY 2

Comparison shopping among savings institutions can be confusing. One of the biggest problems is the terminology. Bank literature has its own vocabulary. Many of the words are familiar ones used in new ways. Others, like abbreviations, may be totally unfamiliar. You, however, have made a start in this area just by reading your text. Prove it to yourself by answering the following questions.

1. a. You know that a compound word is one made up of two separate words. What, however, is compound interest?

_____

_____

   b. You know that a liquid flows freely and can therefore occupy many different types of containers. What, however, are liquid assets?

_____

_____

   c. You know that you and your friends have a mutual interest in rock music. What, however, is a mutual savings bank?

_____

_____

   d. You know that in the problem 320 ÷ 5, the number being divided into five parts is called the dividend. What, however, are credit union dividends?

_____

_____

_____

2. a. The sign at the teller's window says, "Deposits up to $100,000 protected by the FDIC." Where are you? Explain.

_____

_____

_____

   b. You have already signed the check once. Now you are asked to countersign it. What kind of check are you using? Explain.

_____

_____

_____

   c. You hear a banker and a customer talking about the rule of 72. What is the rule of 72?

_____

_____

_____

Chapter 10   *Using Financial Services*

REVIEWING CONSUMER TERMS

Build a crossword puzzle using the terms below. Use the space below to arrange your entries. Then write short definitions for them.

canceled checks

certificate of deposit

certified check

drawee

drawer

electronic fund transfer

endorsement

NOW accounts

payee

reconciling

CHAPTER 10 Using Financial Services

REVIEWING FACTS AND IDEAS

1. Why might a saver choose a certificate of deposit account over a passbook savings account? What disadvantages does it have, if any?

   _____

   _____

   _____

   _____

2. Describe the procedure for reconciling a bank statement.

   _____

   _____

   _____

   _____

3. How does a NOW account differ from most other checking accounts?

   _____

   _____

   _____

   _____

   _____

4. Describe the protective features of traveler's checks.

   _____

   _____

   _____

   _____

   _____

5. List four types of electronic fund transfers.

   _____

   _____

   _____

   _____

   _____

CHAPTER 10   *Using Financial Services*

APPLICATION ACTIVITY 1

You have the following items to deposit in your checking account.

a. Your paycheck: $314.67 (10-37)
b. A birthday check from your grandparents: $100 (19-73)
c. A refund check from a local store: $29.12 (112-28)
d. A personal check from a friend who owed you money: $20 (33-44)
e. A coupon refund check from an out-of-state manufacturer: $1 (3-130)

Fill out the deposit slip below. Your account number is 603-130804. The bank number of each check is provided in parentheses. Note: The bank number usually appears somewhere in the upper righthand portion of a check near the date. The number is the top portion of a fraction and usually contains a hyphen.

WELLS FARGO BANK

CHECKING ACCOUNT NUMBER   DATE

NAME

ADDRESS

X

PLEASE SIGN IN TELLER'S PRESENCE FOR CASH RECEIVED

UNI 125 (6/87)

CHECKING DEPOSIT

CHECKS ARE CREDITED TO YOUR ACCOUNT PENDING FINAL PAYMENT

CURRENCY	$	
COIN		
CHECKS	1	
	2	
TOTAL CHECKS LISTED ON REVERSE		
SUBTOTAL		
◄ LESS CASH		
TOTAL ►		

ADDITIONAL CHECKS PLEASE LIST EACH CHECK SEPARATELY

	$
3	
4	
5	
6	
7	
8	
9	
10	
11	
12	
13	
14	
15	
16	
TOTAL	ENTER THIS TOTAL ON FRONT

CASH COUNT FOR BANK USE

X 100	
X 50	
X 20	
X 10	
X 5	
X 2	
X 1	
TOTAL	$

Decide what kind of endorsement each situation calls for. Label each check in the space provided and endorse accordingly.

1. You receive your paycheck two days before you will be able to deposit it in the bank. You do not like the idea of leaving the check unsigned; if you should lose it, someone might try to forge an endorsement. If you do sign the check, however, and then lose it, someone could cash it. What kind of endorsement should you use?

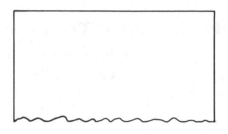

1. _____
   endorsement

2. Instead of banking the check you received from your friend (*d* on the previous page), you use it to pay back your next-door neighbor from whom you borrowed $20 a week earlier. What kind of endorsement should you use?

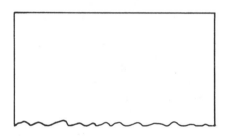

2. _____
   endorsement

3. You are standing at the teller's window in the bank. The teller gives you a pen so that you can endorse the check you want to deposit and reminds you to include your account number. What kind of endorsement should you use?

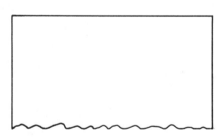

3. _____
   endorsement

4. You need some money for an emergency purchase, one too large to be covered by your check guarantee card. (It has a $100 limit.) You stop by the bank and make out a check to cash. What kind of endorsement should you use?

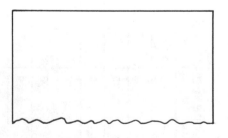

4. _____
   endorsement

CHAPTER **10** *Using Financial Services*

APPLICATION ACTIVITY 2

Enter each of the following transactions in the check register below. Where necessary, fill out one of the blank checks on this or the following page and sign with your own name. Note: Your account number is 603-130804, and you have a balance of $416.68. The last check you filled out was No. 233.

a. March 7: You bought a pair of shoes at Robinson's Department Store for $47.93.
b. March 12: You paid the semiannual premium ($350) on your automobile insurance policy. You are insured by Allstate.
c. March 16: You deposited your paycheck ($314.67) in your checking account.
d. March 20: You picked up a prescription refill at Webster's Pharmacy and paid for it by check ($4).
e. Match 23: You mailed a check to the Department of Water and Power (DWP) to cover your electric bill ($55.06).

		RECORD ALL CHARGES OR CREDITS THAT AFFECT YOUR ACCOUNT						
NUMBER	DATE	DESCRIPTION OF TRANSACTION	PAYMENT/DEBIT (−)	√ T	FEE (IF ANY) (−)	DEPOSIT/CREDIT (+)	BALANCE $	
			$		$	$		

NAME_____   No. _____

ACCOUNT NO._____ _____19____ 16-8/1220

PAY TO THE
ORDER OF_____ | $ _____

_____ DOLLARS

ARCADIA MAIN OFFICE
WELLS FARGO BANK, N.A.
128 E HUNTINGTON DRIVE, ARCADIA, CALIFORNIA 91006

FOR _____

⑈122000247⑈   603130804⑈33

NAME_____ No. _____

ACCOUNT NO._____ _____19____ 16-8/1220

PAY TO THE
ORDER OF_____ $ _____

_____ DOLLARS

ARCADIA MAIN OFFICE

WELLS FARGO BANK, N.A.

128 E. HUNTINGTON DRIVE, ARCADIA, CALIFORNIA 91006

FOR_____

⑆ 1 2 2000 2 4 7 ⑆   6 0 3 1 3 0 8 0 4 ⑈ 3 3

NAME_____ No. _____

ACCOUNT NO._____ _____19____ 16-8/1220

PAY TO THE
ORDER OF_____ $ _____

_____ DOLLARS

ARCADIA MAIN OFFICE

WELLS FARGO BANK, N.A.

128 E. HUNTINGTON DRIVE, ARCADIA, CALIFORNIA 91006

FOR_____

⑆ 1 2 2000 2 4 7 ⑆   6 0 3 1 3 0 8 0 4 ⑈ 3 3

NAME_____ No. _____

ACCOUNT NO._____ _____19____ 16-8/1220

PAY TO THE
ORDER OF_____ $ _____

_____ DOLLARS

ARCADIA MAIN OFFICE

WELLS FARGO BANK, N.A.

128 E. HUNTINGTON DRIVE, ARCADIA, CALIFORNIA 91006

FOR_____

⑆ 1 2 2000 2 4 7 ⑆   6 0 3 1 3 0 8 0 4 ⑈ 3 3

Chapter 11   *Making Investments*

REVIEWING CONSUMER TERMS

Use each of the following terms in a 250-word story entitled "The Day I Wanted to Make an Investment."

bond

capital gain

commission

common stock

maturity date

portfolio

preferred stock

stock

stock exchange

stockbroker

stockholder

_____

_____

_____

_____

_____

_____

_____

_____

_____

_____

_____

_____

_____

_____

_____

_____

_____

_____

_____

_____

_____

_____

_____

_____

_____

_____

_____

_____

Chapter **11** *Making Investments*

REVIEWING FACTS AND IDEAS

1. Describe the role of risk in making investments.

   _____

   _____

   _____

2. What four factors should consumers consider when planning an investment?

   _____

   _____

   _____

3. True or false: Bonds are only issued by corporations.

   _____

   _____

4. List the advantages and disadvantages of owning common and preferred stocks.

   _____

   _____

   _____

5. What is the difference between stocks and bonds?

   _____

   _____

   _____

6. Would you rather have to pay taxes on corporate or municipal bonds? Why?

   _____

   _____

   _____

7. Complete the following statement by selecting the best choice. The wisest investment strategy is to (a) put all your savings into stocks, (b) make sure you have a comfortable income, a good emergency fund, and adequate insurance before you invest in stocks, (c) never buy stocks under any circumstances.

   _____

   _____

   _____

8. Explain how to invest in stocks and bonds.

   _____

   _____

   _____

CHAPTER 11 *Making Investments*

APPLICATION ACTIVITY 1

Using stock market quotations to compute the value of a particular investment is fairly simple. It requires only three basic mathematical operations: multiplication (mostly by round numbers), division (mostly by four—the number of quarters in a year), and decimal conversion (mostly from a half dozen common fractions).

1. Stock prices are quoted in points and fractions thereof. A point equals one dollar. Thus a stock that closes at 24 points is worth $24 a share. What are the dollar equivalents of these closes?

   a. 24-1/4 = $_____   b. 24-1/2 = $_____   c. 24-3/4 = $_____

2. Points are usually divided into eighths. Compute and commit to memory the dollar equivalents of these fractions frequently found in stock market quotations.

   a. 1/8 = $_____   c. 5/8 = $_____

   b. 3/8 = $_____   d. 7/8 = $_____

3. The table below shows the stocks owned by Susan Lazaar, a long-time client of Swiftly, Spiker, & Deferential, Brokers. Study the entries.

Stock	Number of Shares	Purchase Price	Amount Invested
American Stores	25	$46.50	_____
General Motors Corp.	100	53.25	_____
IBM	10	110.00	_____

   a. Complete the table by computing the amount Susan has invested in each stock.

   b. What is the total amount of money Susan has invested in all stocks?   b. _____

   c. If Swiftly, Spike, & Deferential sell the General Motors stock for Susan at 75-1/4, would she make a profit or suffer a loss? (Circle one.) In what amount?   c. _____

4. Jose Garcia owns 200 shares of preferred stock in Illinois Power Company. The dividend on each share is $5 a year and is paid quarterly.

   a. How much does Jose receive each year in dividends?   a. _____

   b. How much does Jose receive each quarter?   b. _____

   c. Assume that Jose has owned the stock for ten years and received dividends every quarter during that time. What is the total amount of dividend income he has received?   c. _____

CHAPTER 11 Making Investments

APPLICATION ACTIVITY 2

Below is a portion of the stock market quotations from *The Wall Street Journal.* It is similar to the illustration that appears in your text. These quotations, however, reflect transactions that took place on October 13, 1995. Compare the two listings. Then answer the questions below.

Quotations as of 5 p.m. Eastern Time
Friday, October 13

52 Weeks Hi	52 Weeks Lo	Stock	Sym	Div	Yld %	PE	Vol 100s	Hi	Lo	Close	Net Chg
				—A—A—A—							
19	11 7/8	AAR	AIR	.48	2.7	24	42	18	17 7/8	17 7/8 –	1/8
27 7/8	19 7/8	ABM Indus.	ABM	.60	2.2	15	13	27	26 7/8	26 7/8 –	1/8
9 7/8	8	ACM GvtFd	ACG	.90	9.2	...	967	9 3/4	9 5/8	9 3/4 +	1/8
7 1/4	6 7/8	ACM OppFd	ADF	.68	9.0	...	129	7 3/8	7 1/4	7 3/16	...
8 7/8	7 1/4	ACM SecFd	GSF	.90	10.3	...	853	8 3/8	8 5/8	8 3/4 +	1/8
7 7/8	5 3/8	ACM SpctmFd	SI	.75	10.9	...	515	7	8 7/8	8 7/8	...
11 1/8	7 3/8	ACM MgmdInc	ADF	1.26	12.8	...	663	9 7/8	9 3/4	9 7/8	...
9 3/8	7 1/2	ACM MgdmcFd	AMF	.90	10.6	...	386	8 3/4	8 1/2	8 1/2 –	1/8
12 1/4	9 1/8	ACM MuniSac	AMU	.90	7.8	...	162	12	11 7/8	11 7/8	...
14 1/2	9 3/8	ADT	ADT		...	17	7186	14 3/8	14 1/8	14 1/8 –	1/8
44 3/4	31 7/8	↑AFLAC	AFL	.52	1.2	13	2771	42 1/2	41 5/8	42 1/4 +	7/8
s 54 5/8	24 5/16	AGCO Cp	AG	.04	.1	7	2427	45 7/8	44 3/8	44 3/8 +	1/8
20 1/8	17	↑AMU Resdntl	AML	1.72	8.8	18	65	19 1/2	19 3/8	19 1/2 +	1/8
s 46 1/4	33 5/8	↓AMP	AMP	.92	2.3	21	6882	40 1/4	39	40 1/4 +	1 1/8
80 1/4	48 3/8	AMR	AMR		...	19	2719	71 1/8	70 3/8	70 7/8 +	3/8
50 1/8	41 1/4	ARCO Chm	RCM	2.80	5.6	10	189	49 7/8	49 3/8	49 3/4 +	3/8
51 1/8	41	ASA	ASA	2.00	4.8	...	377	41 3/4	41 1/4	41 3/4 +	1/4
39 7/8	19 3/4	↑ATT Cap	TCC	.40	1.1	15	1028	37 5/8	37 1/2	37 3/8 +	1/2
86 3/8	47 1/4	AT&T Cp	T	1.32	2.1	20	27696	64 1/4	62 3/8	62 3/8 –	1 1/2
44 3/4	30 1/8	Abbott ab	ABT	.84	2.1	19	17820	40 5/8	40	40 1/8 +	3/8
19	12	Abitibi g	ABY	.20	...	...	3059	17 3/4	16 7/8	17 1/2 +	3/8
18	12 3/8	↑Acceptins	AF		...	11	908	15 1/2	15 1/4	15 1/2	...

52 Weeks Hi	52 Weeks Lo	Stock	Sym	Div	Yld %	PE	Vol 100s	Hi	Lo	Close	Net Chg
				—A—A—A—							
34 3/4	20 3/8	ACE Ltd.	ACL	.56	1.6	8	3415	34	32 3/4	34 +	3/4
29 1/4	9 7/8	AcmeCleve	AMT	.48	1.9	4	1694	25	24 3/4	25 +	1/2
38 3/8	8 1/8	AcmeElec	ACE		...	47	554	9 1/2	8 3/4	9 3/8 +	3/4
34 1/2	23 1/2	↑Acordia	ACO	.72	2.9	12	110	25 1/4	24 3/4	24 3/4 –	1/4
19 3/8	8 3/8	ActavaGp	ACT		...	dd	1521	17 3/8	17 3/8	17 3/8	...
18 3/8	10 1/8	Acuson	ACN		...	33	875	12 3/8	12 1/2	12 1/2 –	1/8
18 7/8	15 3/8	↑AdamsExp	ADX	1.60a	8.6	...	115	18 3/4	18 5/8	18 5/8 +	1/8
39 1/4	22 1/4	↑AdvMicro	AMD		...	10	11224	28 1/2	27 3/8	27 3/8 –	1/8
9 3/8	5	Advest	ADV		...	17	98	9 1/4	9 1/2	9 1/4 +	1/4
↑ 25 1/4	15 1/4	Advo	AD	.10	.4	21	857	25 5/8	25 1/8	25 1/2 +	1/2
13 7/8	10	↑Advocat	AVC		...	14	63	12 1/4	12	12 1/8	...
s 37 1/2	23 3/4	AEGON NV	AEG	.38a	1.0	13	141	37 1/8	38 1/2	37 –	1/4
5 7/8	3 3/8	↑Aeroflex	ARX		...	8	174	4 3/4	4 3/8	4 5/8	...
n 27 7/8	25	AetnaMPS pfA		2. 37	8.6	...	149	27 5/8	27 3/8	27 3/8 +	1/8
75 1/2	42 1/4	AetnaLife	AET	2.76	3.8	52	10627	72 1/2	71	71 3/4 +	1
14 1/8	8 1/4	↑AgnicoEgl	AEM	.10	.7	...	1061	13 1/2	13 1/4	13 3/8 –	1/8
17 3/8	14 1/2	AgreeRlty	ADC	1.80	10.8	13	119	16 7/8	16 3/8	16 5/8 +	1/8
↑ 26 3/8	15 1/4	Ahmanson	AHM	.88	3.2	19	9148	27 1/2	26 3/8	27 1/2 +	7/8
26 3/8	24 1/2	Ahmanson pfB		2.40	9.3	...	14	26	25 7/8	25 7/8	...
↑ 26 1/4	22 1/8	Ahmanson pfC		2.10	8.1	...	232	26 1/2	26	26	...
↑ 58 1/2	39 3/4	Ahmanson pfD		3.00	5.0	...	189	60 1/4	58 1/2	59 3/4 +	1 1/4
38 1/2	28 3/8	Ahold	AHO	.85a	2.3	...	39	37 3/4	37 1/2	37 1/2 –	1/2
59 3/8	43 1/8	AirProduct	APD	1.04	2.0	17	2238	52 1/2	51 5/8	52 1/8 +	3/8
26	18	AirbornFrght	ABF	30	1.2	23	767	24 7/8	24 7/8	24 1/4 +	1/8
30	19 5/8	↑Airgas	ARG		...	23	499	24 7/8	24 1/2	24 1/8 –	1/8
18	10 7/8	Airlease	FLY	2.00a	12.1	12	36	16 1/2	16 3/8	16 1/2 +	1/8
35 3/8	23 7/8	AirTouch	ATI		...	cc	11453	31 1/8	30 1/2	30 5/8 +	3/8

1. Locate Abbott Laboratories (the stock analyzed in your text) in the quotations above. Underline all of its entries.

   a. Is trading in the stock as heavy as it was ten months before? Describe any difference.

   ____

   b. Assume you put off buying the stock in January. Instead you bought in October. How much did the delay cost or save you? Explain.

   ____

   ____

   c. On a daily basis, was the price of the stock fluctuating more or less in October? On what do you base your answer?

   ____

2. Name the stocks having the following features in the table below.

   a. Highest close ____________
   b. Lowest close ____________
   c. Highest volume of shares traded ____________
   d. Lowest volume of shares traded ____________
   e. Highest dividend ____________
   f. Lowest price/earnings ratio ____________

UNIT 3 Lab Money Management: Saving and Investing

SAVING AND INVESTING IN THE REAL WORLD

Unit 3 explains the many ways you can save and invest money. This lab will help you learn more about saving and investing as you interview financial consultants and "ordinary savers" about their saving and investment practices.

TOOLS

1. Newspaper business and front-page sections

2. Business magazines

3. Literature from financial institutions

PROCEDURES

Read the lab in your textbook and complete each activity using the space provided below.

Step A

Financial consultant's name: _____

Telephone number: _____

Interview questions: _____

_____

_____

_____

_____

_____

Step B

Financial consultant 1: _____

Telephone number: _____

Financial consultant 2: _____

Telephone number: _____

_____

_____

Step C

Interview questions:

_____

_____

_____

Step D

Ordinary saver 1: _____

Ordinary saver 2: _____

Ordinary saver 3: _____

Ordinary saver 4: _____

_____

_____

LAB REPORT

Step E

Use your notes from the six interviews to answer the questions below.

1. What was the average percentage of a person's aftertax income the consultants felt should be saved?

    _____

2. What was the average percentage of aftertax income that the savers actually saved?

    _____

3. What was the average size of the savers' emergency funds?

    _____

4. How many savers have current retirement savings plans?

    _____

Step F

Using a word processor or a typewriter, write a 500-word report following the directions given in the Unit 3 Lab in your textbook.

UNIT 4 Types of Credit

ATTITUDE INVENTORY

Before you begin Unit 4, take stock of your attitudes by completing the following inventory. Read each statement and decide how you feel about it—agree, disagree, or undecided. Write your answers in the blanks.

1. Credit is an invention that we could very well do without.

2. Credit is a great way to buy items on impulse.

3. When credit is used, trust is important.

4. Credit is far more important to older people than to young people and young families.

5. Credit usage can be harmful in times of inflation.

6. The government should take a hands-off attitude toward credit transactions.

7. A woman should be granted credit only in the name of her husband.

8. The cost of credit is so small that it may safely be ignored.

9. Wise consumers may sometimes use credit to their advantage.

10. "Borrow cash and save money" is a saying that doesn't make sense.

11. Individuals who open charge accounts can still control their finances.

12. If you cannot save for an item, you don't deserve to own it.

13. Buying on the installment plan is evidence of weak character.

14. Businesses do not like to extend credit.

15. Monthly statements from retail stores are designed to confuse, not aid, the consumer.

1. _____

2. _____

3. _____

4. _____

5. _____

6. _____

7. _____

8. _____

9. _____

10. _____

11. _____

12. _____

13. _____

14. _____

15. _____

RECHECKING YOUR ATTITUDE

Before going on to the next unit, answer the Attitude Inventory questions a second time. Then compare the two sets of responses. On how many statements have your attitudes changed? Can you account for these shifts in your opinions? What do you know now that you did not know then?

1. Credit is an invention that we could very well do without.

2. Credit is a great way to buy items on impulse.

3. When credit is used, trust is important.

4. Credit is far more important to older people than to young people and young families.

5. Credit usage can be harmful in times of inflation.

6. The government should take a hands-off attitude toward credit transactions.

7. A woman should be granted credit only in the name of her husband.

8. The cost of credit is so small that it may safely be ignored.

9. Wise consumers may sometimes use credit to their advantage.

10. "Borrow cash and save money" is a saying that doesn't make sense.

11. Individuals who open charge accounts can still control their finances.

12. If you cannot save for an item, you don't deserve to own it.

13. Buying on the installment plan is evidence of weak character.

14. Businesses do not like to extend credit.

15. Monthly statements from retail stores are designed to confuse, not aid, the consumer.

1. _____
2. _____
3. _____
4. _____
5. _____
6. _____
7. _____
8. _____
9. _____
10. _____
11. _____
12. _____
13. _____
14. _____
15. _____

Answers changed _____ Why? _____

_____

_____

_____

_____

_____

_____

_____

_____

_____

_____

_____

_____

_____

_____

CHAPTER 12 · Commercial and Consumer Credit

REVIEWING CONSUMER TERMS

Write a paragraph that includes the following terms. Use them in ways that demonstrate you know their meaning.

bank card

commercial credit

consumer credit

credit

transaction

_____

_____

_____

_____

_____

_____

_____

_____

_____

_____

_____

_____

_____

_____

_____

_____

_____

_____

_____

_____

_____

_____

_____

_____

_____

_____

_____

_____

CHAPTER **12** Commercial and Consumer Credit

REVIEWING FACTS AND IDEAS

1. What is credit?

   _____

   _____

2. The use of consumer credit began to grow after (a) the Vietnam War, (b) World War I, or (c) World War II.

   _____

   _____

3. Describe how commercial credit can help a business.

   _____

   _____

4. How do commercial and consumer credit differ?

   _____

   _____

5. From the viewpoint of consumers, is credit good or bad? Explain.

   _____

   _____

   _____

6. How does consumer credit affect the prices of consumer goods?

   _____

   _____

   _____

7. Why are young couples inclined to use consumer credit more than older couples?

   _____

   _____

   _____

8. Name four types of credit cards, and tell what kinds of goods and services they can be used to purchase.

   _____

   _____

   _____

   _____

   _____

CHAPTER 12 Commercial and Consumer Credit

APPLICATION ACTIVITY 1

Assume you are a loan officer at Billings National Bank. You are currently considering the four loan applications summarized below. Study them carefully. Then use the questions that follow to help you decide which loans to make. Note: You can only authorize two of the four loans.

A. Arnold Carver is just starting out in the television sales and repair business. He plans to double his stock on hand by purchasing thirty new television sets. Arnold will need about $9,000. He has already talked with a loan officer at Billings National Bank and believes he has a good chance of getting a loan.

B. Cindy Carver is new in town. (She recently moved to Billings to be near her brother Arnold and his wife and children.) Cindy works as a seamstress at the headquarters store of Shopsmart, Inc. The job requires that she commute twenty miles daily. (She drives, since there is no public transportation in Billings.) Unfortunately, moving took a heavy toll on her automobile, which now needs an engine overhaul (total cost $850). Paying cash for the repairs is out of the question for Cindy (moving expenses have eaten up most of her savings). She does not, however, want to ask Arnold for help because she knows that most of his funds are tied up in his business. A loan, it would seem, is her only hope. She decides to try Billings National Bank, the largest financial institution in town.

C. Gilda Manetti is the buyer for the television and stereo department of Shopsmart Membership Stores. (She buys for the main store in Billings and three branches in neighboring communities.) She has just authorized the purchase of 100 color television sets and video cassette recorders. The company treasurer will arrange financing for the transaction, probably with Billings National Bank. Shopsmart has dealt with the bank before. The $35,000 required is a modest sum that should pose no special problems.

D. Paula and Peter Potter want to buy a new color television set and a VCR to go with it. They have shopped around and narrowed their choices to Carver's, a new store offering attractive prices on a limited number of models, and Shopsmart, a membership store having a huge stock and an excellent reputation for service. For the Potters, the purchase is a major one. They hope to finance it with a $1,500 loan from Billings National Bank. They believe the fact that they have their checking and savings accounts with the bank will work in their favor.

1. Which two loans would qualify as consumer credit? Explain why.

_____

_____

_____

_____

_____

2. Which two loans would qualify as commercial credit? Explain why.

_____

_____

_____

_____

_____

3. Of the two business applicants, about whose management skills and debt repayment practices do you know more? Explain.

_____

_____

_____

_____

4. Of the personal-loan applicants, about whose money management skills and debt repayment practices do you know more? Explain.

_____

_____

_____

_____

_____

5. Of the two businesses, which would you say is less likely to have difficulty getting money for loan repayment? Explain.

_____

_____

_____

_____

6. Of the personal-loan applicants, who would you say is less likely to have difficulty getting the money for repayment? Explain.

_____

_____

_____

7. Which applicants have valuable property that could be sold to repay the loan if financial difficulties occurred? Explain.

_____

_____

_____

_____

8. Which two loans would you make? Why?

_____

_____

_____

_____

_____

CHAPTER 12   Commercial and Consumer Credit

APPLICATION ACTIVITY 2

A. Read each of the questions that follow, then write your answer in the space provided.

1. Alexander & Lawson purchased ten dozen sweatshirts at $180 a dozen. Freight on the shipment amounted to $38. What was the total cost of the order?

_____

2. Alexander & Lawson paid for the order within ten days and received a 2 percent discount for doing so.

    a. What was the amount of the cash discount (which applied only to the shirts)?

_____

    b. What was the net cost of the order, including the freight and less the discount?

_____

3. The Video Vault and Games Arcade bought equipment priced at $4,497. The business arranged to pay for the equipment in 12 installments of $470.66.

    a. What was the total cost of the equipment?

_____

    b. How much was the charge for credit?

_____

4. The Boatswain's Gear Store bought equipment priced at $36,510. The seller offered to accept 24 payments of $1,815.15.

    a. What was the installment price of the equipment?

_____

    b. How much of this amount was a charge for credit?

_____

5. Boatswain decided to finance the purchase through a bank. It borrowed $36,510 from the bank and paid cash for the order. Boatswain then paid the bank in 24 installments of $1,728.80.

    a. What was the total amount paid to the bank?

_____

    b. How much of this amount was a charge for credit?

_____

    c. How much did the company save by borrowing from the bank instead of paying the seller in installments?

_____

    d. What was the difference between the seller's charge for credit and the bank's charge for credit?

_____

B. Tej Rahman has been operating an electronics firm for several years. Recently, he feels his sales and profits are not as great as they should be. To attract more customers and to increase sales, he has decided to invite customers to open charge accounts at his store. Up to this time, his business has been operated on a cash basis.

The terms Tej offered to charge customers were generous, and business improved. Tej beamed as he looked over the sales figures each week. All was not well, however. Debts to suppliers were higher than they had ever been, and Tej was having trouble paying them. He even had difficulty meeting his payroll. His friends explained to him that he has a cash flow problem.

Tej talked to his banker, who offered to lend him enough cash to meet his immediate needs. The banker was willing to accept the store's accounts receivables (the amounts owed to the business by the charge customers) as security for the loan. The loan officer agreed to lend Tej an amount equal to 70 percent of the face value of the accounts receivable at an interest rate of 11 percent. If Tej fails to repay the loan, the bank can get its money by collecting the accounts receivable amounts. The first month, the total for the accounts receivable was $82,900.

1. How much money did Tej borrow?

   _____

2. If the entire amount of the loan continues to be outstanding for one month, how much interest will Tej pay (1/12 of one year's interest)?

   _____

3. The second month, accounts receivable equaled $93,000. The quality of the accounts was not as high, however, since some of the credit customers had low credit ratings. The bank agreed to lend only 65 percent. What is the amount of the loan?

   _____

4. If the whole amount borrowed (65 percent of $93,000) was outstanding for the entire month, how much interest did Tej pay?

   _____

5. Another of the bank's customers also was using accounts receivable as security for a loan. Some the accounts were of doubtful value, and the bank would lend only 35 percent of their face value at an interest rate of 13 percent. The accounts receivable totaled $27,000.

   a. How much money did this merchant borrow?

   _____

   b. How much interest did the merchant pay for one month?

   _____

CHAPTER **13** *Consumer Credit Problems*

REVIEWING CONSUMER TERMS

Working in pairs, develop a written script about consumer credit problems. Use all of the terms in your script. Then act out your script in front of the class.

bankruptcy

creditor

discount

disposable income

markup

opportunity cost

pledging

_____

_____

_____

_____

_____

_____

_____

_____

_____

_____

_____

_____

_____

_____

_____

_____

_____

_____

_____

_____

_____

_____

_____

_____

_____

CHAPTER **13** *Consumer Credit Problems*

REVIEWING FACTS AND IDEAS

1. Explain how easy credit can become a problem during a period of inflation.

_____
_____
_____

2. Why are goods likely to cost more at a store after it begins to extend credit?

_____
_____
_____

3. Your neighbors who buy on credit from a local department store may be paying twice for the privilege. For example, they may have to pay interest charges. In what other way do they pay for the use of credit?

_____
_____
_____

4. Which law was passed in an effort to stamp out discrimination in the field of credit?

_____
_____
_____

5. Why do some businesses *not* offer in-house credit but shift the burden to bank card agencies?

_____
_____
_____

6. True or false: If you are a married woman, you may not get a credit card in your birth name (the name you had before you married).

_____
_____

7. Describe deceitful practices used at times by borrowers and lenders.

_____
_____
_____

8. What are three ways consumers can safeguard use of their credit cards?

_____
_____
_____

CHAPTER **13** *Consumer Credit Problems*

APPLICATION ACTIVITY 1

Following are five consumer views of credit. Read each and decide whether you agree or disagree. Explain why.

1. Elaine: "I love credit cards. You can buy what you want when you want, and you don't even feel it. It's like not spending money at all."

_____

_____

_____

_____

2. Arthur: "Using credit sometimes just makes more sense. For example, if I'm going to have to save for, say, a personal computer, then I'd rather have the use of the computer while I'm doing it. You see what I mean?"

_____

_____

_____

_____

3. Preston: "Credit's the only way to go, man. TV, car, stereo, fancy threads—I'm gonna have it all. Afford—what's to afford? The way I look at it, I'm just rentin' the stuff till I lose it. I mean, you gotta enjoy life while you're young—right?"

_____

_____

_____

_____

4. Dina: "Everyone should have a credit card or two. Really, just think about it. If you lose your job or something, that may be the only thing you have to live on."

_____

_____

_____

_____

5. Emily: "I make sure I have a very good reason for pulling out that card. It has to be an emergency or a really special, unexpected purchase before I buy on credit. And nothing small either. If I've got enough to cover it in my wallet, I pay cash.

_____

_____

_____

_____

CHAPTER 13 *Consumer Credit Problems*

APPLICATION ACTIVITY 2

Soon after beginning a new job, Gerald went on a spending spree. In two days, he signed the following credit contracts.

Item	Price	Monthly Payment
Sofa, easy chairs	$1,800	$165.60
Dishwasher	400	36.80
Television set	800	73.60
Stereo	1,000	94.00
Exercise equipment	950	89.30

1. What was the total of Gerald's credit purchases?

1. _____

2. To cover these purchases, how much must Gerald pay out in monthly installments?

2. _____

3. Gerald brings home $832 a month. Experts say that no more than 20 percent of a person's take-home pay should be used for debts.

   a. By this standard, what was the maximum amount Gerald should have earmarked for monthly payments?

   a. _____

   b. By how much has Gerald exceeded this amount?

   b. _____

   c. What percentage of his take home pay has Gerald in fact committed to credit payments?

   c. _____

4. Gerald shares food and housing costs with three co-workers, each contributing $400. Assume his other monthly expenses include $185 for a car payment, $60 for gas, and $15 for the telephone. If Gerald regularly did a budget, what would his calculations be telling him? Be specific.

   _____

   _____

5. a. Suppose Gerald had observed the 20 percent rule described above. Could he have balanced his budget? Again, be specific.

   _____

   _____

   _____

   b. Which of his purchases could he still have made?

   _____

   _____

   _____

CHAPTER **14** *Charge Accounts*

REVIEWING CONSUMER TERMS

Build a crossword puzzle using the terms below. Use the space below to arrange your entries. Then write short definitions for them.

adjusted balance

annual percentage rate

credit rating

finance charge

grace period

line of credit

regular charge account

repossess

revolving charge account

trade-in allowance

CHAPTER 14 *Charge Accounts*

REVIEWING FACTS AND IDEAS

1. What are the six advantages and three disadvantages of charge accounts?

_____

_____

_____

_____

_____

_____

2. What is the difference between a regular and a revolving charge account?

_____

_____

_____

_____

_____

_____

3. What is the purpose of a security agreement?

_____

_____

_____

_____

_____

4. Identify the information found on a monthly statement.

_____

_____

_____

_____

_____

5. What is the first action consumers must take to secure their rights under the Fair Credit Billing Act?

_____

_____

_____

_____

_____

CHAPTER 14 Charge Accounts

APPLICATION ACTIVITY 1

Study the charge account bill that appears below. Then answer the questions on the following page.

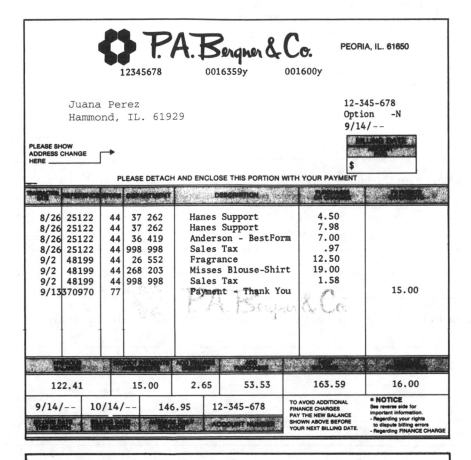

Any **FINANCE CHARGE** added was determined by applying a 1.8% periodic rate **(21.6% ANNUAL RATE)** to the average daily balance. If the average daily minimum **FINANCE CHARGE** of $.50 was applied.

To determine the "average daily balance" we take the beginning balance of your account each day, add any new purchases, and subtract any payments or credits and unpaid finance charges. This gives us the daily balance. Then, we add up all the daily balances for the billing cycle and divide the total by the number days in the billing cycle. This gives us the "average daily balance".

BILLING RIGHTS SUMMARY

In Case of Errors or Questions About Your Bill

If you think your bill is wrong, or if you need more information about a transaction on your bill, write us on a separate sheet at the address shown on your bill as soon as possible. We must hear from you no later than 60 days after we sent you the first bill on which the error or problem appeared. You can telephone us, but doing so will not preserve your rights.

In your letter, give us the following information:

- Your name and account number.
- The dollar amount of the suspected error.
- Describe the error and explain, if you can, why you believe there is an error. If you need more information describe the item you are unsure about.

You do not have to pay any amount in question while we are investigating, but you are still obligated to pay the parts of your bill that are not in question. While we investigate your question,

we cannot report you as delinquent or take any action to collect the amount you question.

Special Rule for Credit Card Purchases

If you have a problem with the quality of goods or services that you purchased with a credit card, and you have tried in good faith to correct the problem with the merchant, you may not have to pay the remaining amount due on the goods or services. You have this protection only when the purchase price was more than $50 and the purchase was made in your home state or within 100 miles of your mailing address. (If we own or operate the merchant, or if we mailed you the advertisement for the property or services, all purchases are covered regardless of amount or location of purchase.)

1. What type of charge account does Juana Perez have? How do you know?

   _____

   _____

   _____

2. What is her regular billing date? _____

3. How many purchases did Juana make in August?_____ in September?_____

4. Make the indicated calculations:

   a. Juana's previous balance was .... $ _____

   b. To which she added purchases of .... + _____

   c. For a total of .... $ _____

   d. On which amount she paid .... − _____

   e. Leaving a balance for the billing period of .... $ _____

   f. Does this figure agree with the new balance on the bill? Why or why not?

      _____

      _____

      _____

5. Which of the methods described in your text was used to calculate the finance charge?

   _____

6. How much interest is the store charging—1.8 percent or 21.6 percent? Explain.

   _____

   _____

   _____

   _____

   _____

7. How could Juana avoid paying additional finance charges?

   _____

   _____

   _____

8. Assume that Juana wishes to make the next payment on her account ($36) by mail. What procedure should she follow?

   _____

   _____

   _____

   _____

   _____

CHAPTER **14** *Charge Accounts*

APPLICATION ACTIVITY 1

When you sign an application to open a charge account, you are doing more than asking for credit. You are promising to observe the terms of the card's security agreement. These terms are usually detailed in a brochure mailed to you with your card. Some sample provisions from a credit agreement for a retail store are reproduced below. Read them carefully. Then answer the questions on the following page.

AGREEMENT AND FEDERAL TRUTH IN LENDING DISCLOSURE STATEMENT

Annual Percentage Rate	Grace Period	Method of Computing Balance	Annual Fees	Minimum Finance Charge	Late Fees
21.6% (1.8% per month)	25 days	Average daily balance	None	$0.50	None

Terms of Payment. I promise to pay the total of all transactions which I make and which others make with my permission on this account. I will receive a billing statement each month in which there is a balance owing on my account (called "New Balance" on the statement). I agree to pay the New Balance, or the Minimum Payment Due, within 25 days of the closing date shown on the statement. The Minimum Payment will be (a) 1/5 of the New Balance, plus past-due amounts, or (b) $10, whichever is greater. If my New Balance is less than $10, however, the Minimum Payment Due will be equal to the New Balance.

Imposition of Finance Charges. If I fail to pay the New Balance shown on my monthly billing statement within 25 days of the closing period, I agree to pay the Finance Charge computed on the Average Daily Balance for the billing cycle covered by the statement. The "Average Daily Balance" is the sum of all balances outstanding at the end of each day in the billing cycle divided by the number of days in the cycle. The outstanding balance is calculated by adding purchases and other charges posted to my account for each day and, from that amount subtracting payments or credits posted to the account for that day, excluding any unpaid Finance Charges. All payments and credits will be applied first to unpaid Finance Charges and then to the oldest unpaid purchases.

Amount of Finance Charges. The Finance Charge will be calculated by applying a rate of 1.8% per month (ANNUAL PERCENTAGE RATE OF 21.6%) to the Average Daily Balance. If the Finance Charge computed by this method is less than $0.50, I will pay a Finance Charge of $0.50 for the billing cycle.

Security Interest. To secure the payment of the amounts owing on merchandise purchases, the Company will retain a security interest in all purchases. Payments on my account will be applied first to unpaid Finance Charges, then to unpaid purchases in the order in which they were posted to my account. The security interest on each item of merchandise will terminate when the price of that item has been paid in full. Under this agreement, the Company is authorized to file, and sign on my behalf, a financing statement in connection with any items under a security interest held by the Company.

Means of Payment. I agree to pay the Company with Currency, with a check drawn on a United States bank and payable in United States dollars, or with a money order payable in United States dollars. If the Company accepts payment made in some

other form, I understand that such payment will be not credited to my account until converted to a form previously mentioned or until the third day after receipt, whichever is sooner. I agree that the Company may charge my account for costs incurred to convert my payment. I agree that the Company may charge my account up to $10 to cover collection costs for any check or draft that is not honored for the full amount.

Default. If I fail to comply with any of the terms or conditions of this Agreement, I will be in default and the Company may declare the entire balance of my account, including any applicable Finance Charge, due and payable at once and pursue its legal remedies to effect collection. If I fail to make payments as required and my account is referred to an attorney or collection agency for collection, I agree to pay the reasonable fees of such attorney or collection agency and all court costs to the extent permitted by law. No waiver by the Company of any default hereunder shall constitute a waiver of any other default.

Credit Card. The credit card issued under this Agreement is loaned to me and remains the property of the Company, and it will be surrendered upon request. I understand that the Company has no obligation to extend to me any credit and may refuse, without prior notice, to allow any purchase or charge on my account.

Applicable Law. The laws of the State of Ohio shall govern the construction and enforcement of this Agreement. Any provision of this Agreement that may be prohibited by law shall be ineffective only to the extent of such restriction.

Assignment. The Company may amend this Agreement upon the giving of notice, if any, as required by law. The Company may assign its rights to this Agreement without prior notice to me.

Credit Investigation and Reporting. I hereby authorize the Company to investigate the references, statements, and other data provided in my application or obtained from me or any other person pertaining to my credit responsibility. I will furnish further information as requested. I authorize the Company to report its credit experience with me to credit reporting agencies and others who have a legal right to receive such information.

Annual Fees. I understand that no annual fee is to be applied to this account.

1. Assume that your first monthly statement shows a balance of $168.20. What rules in the credit agreement apply to the calculation of the minimum monthly payment required?

   _____

   _____

   _____

2. Using the balance of $168.20, calculate the amount of your minimum monthly payment.

   _____

3. You want to buy a $355 airline ticket. Can you put the purchase on your credit card? Why or why not?

   _____

   _____

   _____

4. Based on the credit agreement, what is the monthly interest rate you will be charged on unpaid balances? the annual rate?

   _____

   _____

   _____

5. Your only additional purchase for the second month's bill was a portable television set for $262. Assume that you made only the minimum monthly payment calculated in question 2 above.

   a. What is the amount carried over from the previous month's balance?

   _____

   b. What is the amount of the finance charge on the previous month's balance?

   _____

   c. What is the new balance for this month?

   _____

   d. What is the new minimum payment for this monthly statement?

   _____

6. If you had a balance of $24 carried over to the next month, what is the amount of the finance charge you would pay? Explain.

   _____

   _____

   _____

7. Which part of the credit agreement protects the store's interests if you fail to pay make your monthly payments?

   _____

   _____

   _____

CHAPTER **15** *Installment Credit*

REVIEWING CONSUMER TERMS

Write a paragraph incorporating the following terms.

acceleration clause

add-on clause

balloon payment

closed-end credit

down payment

garnishment

installment credit

prorated

rule of 78s

sales finance company

security interest

_____

_____

_____

_____

_____

_____

_____

_____

_____

_____

_____

_____

_____

_____

_____

_____

_____

_____

_____

_____

_____

_____

_____

_____

CHAPTER **15** *Installment Credit*

REVIEWING FACTS AND IDEAS

1. How does installment credit differ from open-end credit?

   _____

   _____

   _____

   _____

   _____

2. Identify five installment credit problems.

   _____

   _____

   _____

   _____

   _____

3. Do you consider the balloon clause fair if it is printed in boldface type in the contract?

   _____

   _____

   _____

4. Describe the add-on clause. Would you be willing to buy merchandise under terms of a contract containing such a clause?

   _____

   _____

   _____

   _____

5. What is a garnishment, and why has it been the object of special legislation?

   _____

   _____

   _____

6. What is the rule of thumb for how much debt a consumer can manage?

   _____

   _____

   _____

CHAPTER 15 Installment Credit

APPLICATION ACTIVITY 1

Decide whether the situations described below are instances of installment or open-end credit. Label each accordingly and explain the reason(s) for your choice.

1. Your mother gives you her bank card for one day. She tells you to use the card to (a) pay your quarterly tuition at school, (b) fill up the gas tank in the family car, and (c) purchase two posters at a local framing shop.

   _____ credit: _____

   _____

   _____

2. You work as a salesclerk in a stereo outlet. A customer is interested in buying $3,000 worth of recording equipment. It is store policy to require 20 percent down and full payment within eighteen months. Your customer agrees and asks you to compute the monthly payment based on an eighteen-month term.

   _____ credit: _____

   _____

   _____

3. Your neighbor awakes one morning to find his car missing from the driveway. He calls the police but they refuse to list the vehicle as stolen. Your neighbor, it turns out, is behind in his car payments. The police suspect that the vehicle has been repossessed. They suggest your neighbor call the dealership where he purchased the car.

   _____ credit: _____

   _____

   _____

4. You are writing checks for your monthly bills. You bought several gifts in April and now your purchases are beginning to show up in your department store statements. Because the amounts are so large, you decide to pay only one bill in full. On all the others, you make only the minimum payment.

   _____ credit: _____

   _____

   _____

5. Your sister, a computer animator, desperately needs a vacation. (She has been working ten hours a day, seven days a week for four months to produce a film for a client.) She borrows $2,000 from a bank and flies off to Tahiti. "I'll worry about $110 a month plus interest for the next year and a half," she sighs. "For the next two weeks, though, I'm worrying about nothing."

   _____ credit: _____

   _____

   _____

CHAPTER **15** *Installment Credit*

APPLICATION ACTIVITY 2

Laurie Chew borrowed $1,200 from the bank at 18 percent interest. She agreed to repay the loan in twelve monthly installments of $109.75 each ($100 in principal and $9.75 in interest). Just after making her fourth payment, Laurie closed a big deal at work. As a result, she received a $1,000 commission in addition to her regular salary check. Laurie decided to use part of the money to pay off her loan early. She calculated that this would save her nearly $80 (8 × $9.75 = $78). When Laurie went to the bank, however, she discovered that her savings came to much less than that amount. Why? Because the loan agreement contained a Rule-of-78s clause. Help Laurie understand how the rule works.

1. a. Laurie's original payment plan called for how many installments?   a. _____

    b. Find the sum of all the digits representing the payments: 12 + 11 + 10 +
       9 + 8 + 7 + 6 + 5 + 4 + 3 + 2 + 1 =   b. _____

2. During the first month of the loan, Laurie had the use of the full $1,200. She therefore owed the bank 12/78 of the total interest.

    a. At the end of the first month, Laurie paid back $100 of the principal. How much of the original $1,200 did she still have for her own use?   a. _____

    b. For the second month of the loan, how much additional interest did Laurie owe?   b. _____

    c. Starting with these figures, complete the chart.

End of . . .	Principal ($)		Interest Earned by Bank (fraction)
	Total Paid	Still Owed	
First month	100		12/78
Second month			
Third month			
Fourth month			

3. a. What was the total projected amount of interest on Laurie's loan? (12 × 9.75 = ?)   a. _____

    b. What portion of the interest had the bank earned after four months? (12/78 + 11/78 + 10/78 + 9/78 = ?)   b. _____

    c. This fraction translates into what dollar amount? (Hint: 3a × 3b = 3c)   c. _____

    d. How much interest had Laurie actually paid after four months? (4 × 9.75 = ?)   d. _____

    e. Had Laurie overpaid or underpaid interest at that point? By how much? (*Hint*: Compare 3c and 3d.) Show your computations in the margin.   e. _____

UNIT 4 LAB Types of Credit

BUYING ON CREDIT

Unit 4 discusses the various types of consumer credit and explains the positive and negative aspects for the consumer regarding the use of credit. Completing this lab will show you how using credit to purchase a big-ticket furniture item affects the personal economics of two imaginary consumers.

TOOLS
1. Consumer and business magazines
2. Home decoration and family living magazines
3. Newspaper and direct-mail ads from furniture and department stores

PROCEDURES
Read the lab in your textbook and complete each activity using the space provided below.

Step A
Consumer #1: _____

_____

_____

Consumer #2: _____

_____

_____

Step B
Furniture Store #1: _____

Telephone number: _____

Furniture Store #2: _____

Telephone number: _____

Department Store: _____

Telephone number: _____

Step C
Furniture selection for consumer #1: _____

_____

Furniture selection for consumer #2: _____

_____

Step D

Credit Payments for Furniture Purchase			
	Purchase Price	Finance Charge	Monthly Payment	Amount of Monthly Interest
Store A				
Store B				
Store C				

LAB REPORT
Step E

Use your notes and credit payment charts to answer the questions below.

1. What would be the total dollar amount of the interest charges for Consumer 1's and Consumer 2's table and chair set at Store A? at Store B? at Store C? (Assume that the consumer will take the entire installment period to complete payments.)

_____

_____

_____

2. What percentage of Consumer 1's and Consumer 2's monthly take-home pay will be devoted to credit debt if he or she purchases the furniture set from Store A? from Store B? from Store C? (Remember to include the open and closed-end credit you listed in your consumer profile as well as the debt caused by the furniture purchase.)

_____

_____

_____

Step F

Using a word processor or a typewriter, write a two-page report describing the advantages and the opportunity costs of using credit to buy a big ticket item such as a table and chair set. Use your imaginary consumers as specific examples of the personal economic impact of credit use. In your report, state your choice of the furniture set, store, and installment contract that would be best for each consumer. Explain the reasons for your choices.

UNIT 5 Getting and Keeping Credit

ATTITUDE INVENTORY

Before you begin Unit 5, take stock of your attitudes by completing the following inventory. Read each statement and decide how you feel about it—agree, disagree, or undecided. Write your answers in the blanks.

1. Since young people are almost always denied credit, they should not waste their time by applying for it.

1. _____

2. There is no point in reading a credit contract because the average consumer would not understand it anyway.

2. _____

3. Credit bureaus tend to do more harm than good.

3. _____

4. The consumer who needs to borrow money would do well to avoid banks as a source for funds.

4. _____

5. Loan sharks serve no useful purpose.

5. _____

6. Declaring yourself bankrupt is a good, painless, and legal way to avoid paying your debts.

6. _____

7. Charging interest for a loan is unethical.

7. _____

8. Consumers are at a disadvantage because they cannot shop around for credit.

8. _____

9. A businessperson who is asked to extend credit has a right to ask how much the applicant earns each month.

9. _____

10. Credit is easy to get if you do not need it.

10. _____

11. If you get hopelessly in debt, the best thing to do is move to another town and start over again with a clean record.

11. _____

12. A good credit rating is not important to a consumer who has formed a habit of paying cash for purchases.

12. _____

13. Finance companies charge too much interest.

13. _____

14. There are times when it makes good sense to borrow against an insurance policy.

14. _____

RECHECKING YOUR ATTITUDE

Before going on to the next unit, answer the Attitude Inventory questions a second time. Then compare the two sets of responses. On how many statements have your attitudes changed? Can you account for these shifts in your opinions? What do you know now that you did not know then?

1. Since young people are almost always denied credit, they should not waste their time by applying for it.

   1. _____

2. There is no point in reading a credit contract because the average consumer would not understand it anyway.

   2. _____

3. Credit bureaus tend to do more harm than good.

   3. _____

4. The consumer who needs to borrow money would do well to avoid banks as a source for funds.

   4. _____

5. Loan sharks serve no useful purpose.

   5. _____

6. Declaring yourself bankrupt is a good, painless, and legal way to avoid paying your debts.

   6. _____

7. Charging interest for a loan is unethical.

   7. _____

8. Consumers are at a disadvantage because they cannot shop around for credit.

   8. _____

9. A businessperson who is asked to extend credit has a right to ask how much the applicant earns each month.

   9. _____

10. Credit is easy to get if you do not need it.

    10. _____

11. If you get hopelessly in debt, the best thing to do is move to another town and start over again with a clean record.

    11. _____

12. A good credit rating is not important to a consumer who has formed a habit of paying cash for purchases.

    12. _____

13. Finance companies charge too much interest.

    13. _____

14. There are times when it makes good sense to borrow against an insurance policy.

    14. _____

Answers changed _____ Why? _____

_____

_____

_____

_____

_____

_____

_____

_____

_____

_____

_____

_____

CHAPTER **16** *Evaluating Credit Terms and Establishing Credit*

REVIEWING CONSUMER TERMS

Use the following terms in a 250-word paper on evaluating credit terms and establishing credit.

credit bureau

credit disclosure form

debtor

credit references

Fair Credit Reporting Act

Fair Debt Collection Practices Act

investigative reporting

right of rescission

Truth-in-Lending Act

_____

_____

_____

_____

_____

_____

_____

_____

_____

_____

_____

_____

_____

_____

_____

_____

_____

_____

_____

_____

_____

_____

_____

_____

_____

_____

CHAPTER 16 Evaluating Credit Terms and Establishing Credit

REVIEWING FACTS AND IDEAS

1. The Truth-in-Lending Act was passed because (a) merchants demanded regulation, (b) banks required stricter standards, or (c) consumers were confused about the cost of credit.

_____

2. The Truth-in-Lending Act requires that you be told what two very important facts when applying for credit?

_____

_____

3. What is the right of rescission?

_____

_____

4. Identify the three C's of credit.

_____

_____

5. List five questions usually asked on credit application forms.

_____

_____

_____

6. True or false: A credit bureau assigns credit ratings to consumers.

_____

_____

7. What is the purpose of the Fair Credit Reporting Act?

_____

_____

_____

8. List five of the fifteen consumer rights.

_____

_____

_____

_____

_____

_____

CHAPTER 16 Evaluating Credit Terms and Establishing Credit

APPLICATION ACTIVITY 1

You have just purchased a new tape deck. Below is a copy of the disclosure statement given to you by the store. Study the form. Then answer the questions that follow.

ANNUAL PERCENTAGE RATE The cost of your credit as a yearly rate.	FINANCE CHARGE The dollar amount the credit will cost you.	Amount Financed The amount of credit provided to you or on your behalf.	Total of Payments The amount you will have paid after you have made all payments as scheduled.	Total Sale Price The total cost of your purchase on credit, including your downpayment of $ 25.00
14.5 %	$ 34.66	$ 237.50	$ 272.16	$ 297.16

You have the right to receive at this time an itemization of the Amount Financed.
☐ I want an itemization.   ☒ I do not want an itemization.

Your payment schedule will be:

Number of Payments	Amount of Payments	When Payments Are Due
12	$22.68	Monthly, beginning March 1

Insurance
Credit life insurance and credit disability insurance are not required to obtain credit, and will not be provided unless you sign and agree to pay the additional cost.

Type	Premium	Signature
Credit Life		I want credit life insurance. Signature
Credit Disability		I want credit disability insurance. Signature
Credit Life and Disability		I want credit life and disability insurance. Signature

Security: You are giving a security interest in:
☒ the goods or property being purchased.
☐

Filing fees $ _____   Non-filing insurance $ _____

Late Charge: If a payment is late, you will be charged $ 5.00

Prepayment: If you pay off early, you
☐ may   ☐ will not   have to pay a penalty.
☒ may   ☐ will not   be entitled to a refund of part of the finance charge.

See your contract documents for any additional information about nonpayment, default, any required repayment in full before the scheduled date, and prepayment refunds and penalties.

_____
e means an estimate

1. What was the purchase price of the tape deck? Explain how you arrived at that figure.

   _____

   _____

   _____

2. What is the total finance charge?

   _____

3. By mid-August, how much will you have paid on the tape deck? How long will it take to pay for the tape deck in full?

   _____

4. If you are late in making a payment, how much will you be charged?

   _____

5. A friend of yours bought a similar tape deck at another store. The monthly credit charge was 1.7 percent? Who got the better deal—you or your friend? Explain.

   _____

   _____

   _____

   _____

6. You sell a short article to the local newspaper for $100. You would like to use the money to pay off the tape deck early. Will you benefit or lose by doing so? Explain.

   _____

   _____

   _____

   _____

7. The disclosure form has a space for the borrower to sign up for credit life insurance.

   a. Who pays for credit life insurance?

   _____

   _____

   _____

   b. Why do you think someone would take out credit life insurance when signing an installment loan?

   _____

   _____

   _____

   _____

CHAPTER 16 Evaluating Credit Terms and Establishing Credit

APPLICATION ACTIVITY 2

When evaluating credit terms, you will want to know the total amount to be financed, the interest rate, and the total amount to be repaid. Read each of the examples below, then calculate the credit amounts.

1. Find the total amount to be paid in each of the following examples.

   a. 12 payments at $25 each

   b. 18 payments at $36.98 each

   c. $118.33 a month paid over a period of 25 months

2. Find the total finance charge in each situation.

   a. $800 borrowed, $875 to be repaid

   b. $115 financed, $133 to be repaid

   c. $17,893 to be repaid, $14,330 financed

3. Find the number of hundreds in the amount financed.

   a. $1,200 financed

   b. $300 financed

   c. $26,344 financed

4. Find the finance charge per hundred for each $100 financed.

   a. Finance charge of $160, 20 hundreds in the amount financed

   b. Finance charge of $788, 24 hundreds in the amount financed

   c. Finance charge of $52, 6.5 hundreds in the amount financed

5. Merchants who extend credit must tell customers the annual percentage rate the store is charging. Once you know the annual percentage rate (APR), you can use interest tables to calculate the amount that you will repay for each $100 borrowed. Look at the interest table below. The percentages across the table represent annual percentage rates. The numbers down the side on the left represent the number of payments that will be made to repay the amount borrowed and the finance charge. Assume that you are borrowing $1,400 at an APR of 12.5 percent, and you will repay the loan in 12 payments. Find the 12.5 percent column, then the 12 row in the "Number of Payments" column. The intersection where the row and column meet shows an amount of 6.90. You will pay a finance charge of $6.90 for each $100 borrowed. In this example, you are borrowing $1,400, which equals 14 hundreds. Multiplying $6.90 times 14 gives you a finance charge of $96.60. You could also find the APR if you knew the number of payments and the finance charge per $100.

ANNUAL PERCENTAGE RATE TABLE FOR MONTHLY PAYMENT PLANS
SEE INSTRUCTIONS FOR USE OF TABLES

FRB-103-M

NUMBER OF PAYMENTS	ANNUAL PERCENTAGE RATE															
	10.00%	10.25%	10.50%	10.75%	11.00%	11.25%	11.50%	11.75%	12.00%	12.25%	12.50%	12.75%	13.00%	13.25%	13.50%	13.75%
	(FINANCE CHARGE PER $100 OF AMOUNT FINANCED)															
1	0.83	0.85	0.87	0.90	0.92	0.94	0.96	0.98	1.00	1.02	1.04	1.06	1.08	1.10	1.12	1.15
2	1.25	1.28	1.31	1.35	1.38	1.41	1.44	1.47	1.50	1.53	1.57	1.60	1.63	1.66	1.69	1.72
3	1.67	1.71	1.76	1.80	1.84	1.88	1.92	1.96	2.01	2.05	2.09	2.13	2.17	2.22	2.26	2.30
4	2.09	2.14	2.20	2.25	2.30	2.35	2.41	2.46	2.51	2.57	2.62	2.67	2.72	2.78	2.83	2.88
5	2.51	2.58	2.64	2.70	2.77	2.83	2.89	2.96	3.02	3.08	3.15	3.21	3.27	3.34	3.40	3.46
6	2.94	3.01	3.08	3.16	3.23	3.31	3.38	3.45	3.53	3.60	3.68	3.75	3.83	3.90	3.97	4.05
7	3.36	3.45	3.53	3.62	3.70	3.78	3.87	3.95	4.04	4.12	4.21	4.29	4.38	4.47	4.55	4.64
8	3.79	3.88	3.98	4.07	4.17	4.26	4.36	4.46	4.55	4.65	4.74	4.84	4.94	5.03	5.13	5.22
9	4.21	4.32	4.43	4.53	4.64	4.75	4.85	4.96	5.07	5.17	5.28	5.39	5.49	5.60	5.71	5.82
10	4.64	4.76	4.88	4.99	5.11	5.23	5.35	5.46	5.58	5.70	5.82	5.94	6.05	6.17	6.29	6.41
11	5.07	5.20	5.33	5.45	5.58	5.71	5.84	5.97	6.10	6.23	6.36	6.49	6.62	6.75	6.88	7.01
12	5.50	5.64	5.78	5.92	6.06	6.20	6.34	6.48	6.62	6.76	6.90	7.04	7.18	7.32	7.46	7.60
13	5.93	6.08	6.23	6.38	6.53	6.68	6.84	6.99	7.14	7.29	7.44	7.59	7.75	7.90	8.05	8.20
14	6.36	6.52	6.69	6.85	7.01	7.17	7.34	7.50	7.66	7.82	7.99	8.15	8.31	8.48	8.64	8.81
15	6.80	6.97	7.14	7.32	7.49	7.66	7.84	8.01	8.19	8.36	8.53	8.71	8.88	9.06	9.23	9.41
16	7.23	7.41	7.60	7.78	7.97	8.15	8.34	8.53	8.71	8.90	9.08	9.27	9.46	9.64	9.83	10.02
17	7.67	7.86	8.06	8.25	8.45	8.65	8.84	9.04	9.24	9.44	9.63	9.83	10.03	10.23	10.43	10.63
18	8.10	8.31	8.52	8.73	8.93	9.14	9.35	9.56	9.77	9.98	10.19	10.40	10.61	10.82	11.03	11.24
19	8.54	8.76	8.98	9.20	9.42	9.64	9.86	10.08	10.30	10.52	10.74	10.96	11.18	11.41	11.63	11.85
20	8.98	9.21	9.44	9.67	9.90	10.13	10.37	10.60	10.83	11.06	11.30	11.53	11.76	12.00	12.23	12.46

a. Use the table to find the APR if you have 15 payments with a finance charge of $8.71 per $100 financed.

_____

b. Find the total finance charge for $600 to be paid back in 9 payments and with an APR of 10.25 percent.

_____

c. Find the APR if you have 8 payments with a finance charge of $5.22 per $100 financed.

_____

Chapter 17 Borrowing Money

REVIEWING CONSUMER TERMS

Explain in writing how each of the following terms relates to borrowing money.

beneficiary
consolidation loan
consumer finance company
loan sharks

_____

_____

_____

_____

_____

_____

_____

_____

_____

_____

_____

_____

_____

_____

_____

_____

_____

_____

_____

_____

_____

_____

_____

_____

_____

_____

_____

_____

CHAPTER **17** *Borrowing Money*

REVIEWING FACTS AND IDEAS

1. Explain how one may "save money by borrowing money" when buying on credit.

   _____

   _____

   _____

   _____

2. Name three savings institutions that provide cash loans.

   _____

   _____

   _____

   _____

3. Why are bank interest rates low compared to those of some other lenders?

   _____

   _____

   _____

   _____

4. Explain why consumer finance companies have to charge higher rates of interest than banks.

   _____

   _____

   _____

   _____

   _____

5. What is a consolidation loan?

   _____

   _____

   _____

   _____

6. If you borrow money from an insurance company, using your policy as collateral, what happens to your insurance protection?

   _____

   _____

   _____

   _____

CHAPTER 17 Borrowing Money

APPLICATION ACTIVITY 1

Complete the crossword puzzle by using vocabulary words and familiar terms from this and the previous unit. Then answer the questions on the next page.

Across

1. Finance company specialty: _____ loans
5. Organization that rates consumers: credit _____
7. Cost of credit (two words)
10. Person unable to pay his or her debts
12. A consumer's reputation; one of the three C's of credit
15. A charge account generally paid in full each month
16. Installment buying: _____-end credit
18. Canceling a contract; exercising the right of _____
19. Creditor sets payments; _____ contract

Down

1. Alternative to credit: paying _____
2. _____ in Lending
3. Bank or store with which a consumer has done business on credit
4. Saving/lending institution sponsored by an employer for employees': credit _____
6. Annual percentage rate (abbreviation)
8. Property owned by a consumer; one of the three C's of credit
9. Period generally quoted for an interest rate
11. Period within which to pay a credit bill without owing interest
12. Ability to pay debts from income; one of the three C's of credit
13. Fair Credit Billing _____
14. A loan with a large payment at the end
17. Type of credit; _____-ended

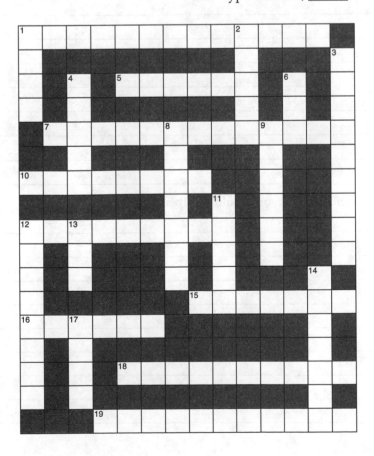

1. When is a consolidation loan most appropriate?

_____

_____

_____

_____

_____

_____

2. What is a loan shark, and why should you avoid one?

_____

_____

_____

_____

_____

3. If you were planning to buy a new car, would you finance its purchase at a consumer finance company, a bank, or a credit union? Rank the loan sources as your first, second, and third choice. Give reasons for your choices.

_____

_____

_____

_____

_____

_____

4. Explain a private loan and how you would set up and repay such a loan.

_____

_____

_____

_____

_____

_____

_____

CHAPTER **17** *Borrowing Money*

APPLICATION ACTIVITY 2

When applying for a loan, you will have to fill out a form that tells the lender about you and your financial circumstances. Fill out the loan application below, basing your entries on your own personal information (for example, your name, address, social security number, and so on) and the personal information given below.

You want to buy a $12,000 car and will finance it through your bank with a down payment of $2,400. You have not borrowed previously from the Safe and Sure Bank, but you maintain savings and checking accounts there. Your birthdate is 1-1-73, and you have been an agent in your city for Bentford Insurance Co., 5 Main Street, for three years. Your net income is $15,000 per year. It is your first job. Your spouse has been the office manager for the same company for two years, has a net salary of $12,000 per year and was born 3-17-73. Your spouse will be a cosigner on the loan.

You are renting an apartment from Townhouses Inc. and have lived there two years. Your rent is $450 per month. You previously lived with your parents. You presently own a three-year-old Tempo automobile, which you bought through Home Town National Bank. Your debts include $300 to Appliance Outlets (original amount was $520) and $250 to Doctors Hospital (original amount was $1,360). You make monthly payments of $40 to each of these creditors.

Adapted from "Banking is . . .," a publication of National Learning Productions, Inc., St. Albans, WV 25177.

Safe & Sure Bank
APPLICATION FOR CREDIT

PURPOSE OF LOAN _____ AMOUNT OF LOAN REQUESTED $_____ NO. OF MONTHS _____

APPLICANT		DATE BORN	DEPENDENTS	RESIDENCE PHONE	

ADDRESS— STREET	CITY		STATE	ZIP	YEARS	MONTHS

MORTGAGE HOLDER OR LANDLORD	ADDRESS	PURCHASE PRICE $	MTG. OR RENT PMT.
		MORTGAGE BAL. $	

PREVIOUS ADDRESS	YEARS	MONTHS

EMPLOYMENT-- FIRM	APPLICANT	ADDRESS	YEARS	MONTHS

PHONE	POSITION	SOCIAL SECURITY NUMBER	NET SALARY MO. YR.

PREVIOUS EMPLOYMENT	ADDRESS	YEARS	MONTHS

OTHER INCOME--SOURCE (alimony, child support and maintenance income need not be disclosed)	NET INCOME MO. YR.

RELATIVE --- RELATIONSHIP --- (NOT LIVING WITH)	ADDRESS	PHONE NUMBER	ADV. or B.R.

BANK (APPLICANTS)	OFFICE ADDRESS	CHECKING ☐ SAVINGS ☐	ACCOUNT NO.

CREDIT REFERENCES — LIST BELOW ALL LOAN OBLIGATIONS NOW OWING OR RECENTLY PAID (IF NONE STATE "NONE")

NAME	ADDRESS OR BRANCH	ORIGINAL AMT.	UNPAID BALANCE	MONTHLY INSTAL.

OTHER OBLIGATIONS -- ALIMONY, CHILD SUPPORT, MAINTENANCE, ETC.

AUTO OWNED (MAKE AND YEAR)	FINANCED BY	MASTER CARD No	VISA CARD No	CR.

INSURANCE COMPANY -- AUTO	AGENT	ADDRESS	PHONE	T

IF YOU AND ANOTHER PERSON (FOR INSTANCE, YOUR SPOUSE) WISH TO APPLY FOR JOINT CREDIT (THAT IS, YOU WILL BOTH USE OR BE CONTRACTUALLY LIABLE UPON THE SAME ACCOUNT) PLEASE PROVIDE US WITH THE FOLLOWING INFORMATION, AND ASK HIM OR HER TO SIGN BELOW UNDER YOUR SIGNATURE.

CO-BORROWER		DATE BORN	DEPENDENTS	RELATIONSHIP TO BORROWER	RESIDENCE PHONE

ADDRESS STREET	CITY		STATE	ZIP	YEARS	MONTHS

EMPLOYMENT FIRM	CO-BORROWER	ADDRESS	YEARS	MONTHS

PHONE	POSITION	SOCIAL SECURITY NUMBER	NET SALARY MO. YR.

OTHER INCOME SOURCE (alimony, child support and maintenance income need not be disclosed)

RELATIVE RELATIONSHIP (NOT LIVING WITH)

CREDIT REFERENCES	ADDRESS OR BRANCH	ORIGINAL AMT.	UNPAID BALANCE	MONTHLY INSTAL.

OTHER OBLIGATIONS ALIMONY, CHILD SUPPORT, MAINTENANCE, ETC.

Undersigned hereby authorizes you or any credit bureau or other investigation agency employed by you to investigate any reference given by undersigned or statements or other data obtained from undersigned or from any other person pertaining to undersigned's credit and financial responsibility. Undersigned also authorizes you to furnish to other persons. upon request. information concerning undersigned's credit and financial transactions or experiences with the Bank

The undersigned acknowledges that I (we) have been provided with a retainable copy of the notices indicating the Federal and State agencies that enforce compliance by the Bank with the Federal and State prohibitions against discrimination on the basis of sex, marital status, race, color, religion, national origin and ancestry.

Undersigned understands and agrees that the provisions on the reverse side hereof, which are hereby incorporated herein by reference. constitute a part of this agreement

I PREFER TO HAVE MY PAYMENTS FALL DUE ON THE (CIRCLE ONE) 5 10 15 20 25 30 STARTING_____ 19____

DATE _____ APPLICANT _____

           CO-BORROWER _____

Unit  LAB Getting and Keeping Credit

THE SEARCH FOR GOOD CREDIT

Unit 5 outlines consumers' rights and responsibilities when establishing credit and borrowing money. In this lab, you will extend your study of consumer credit rights and learn more about evaluating loan offers.

TOOLS

1. Business and consumer magazines
2. Financial textbooks
3. Newspaper business sections

PROCEDURES

Read the lab in your textbook and complete each activity using the space provided below.

Step A

Bank or savings and loan #1: _____

	Loan Amount	Number of Payments	Payment Amount	Payment Period	Annual Percentage Rate (APR)	Total Finance Charge (TFC)
Institution A						
Institution B						
Institution C						
Credit Union						

Bank or savings and loan #2: _____

	Loan Amount	Number of Payments	Payment Amount	Payment Period	Annual Percentage Rate (APR)	Total Finance Charge (TFC)
Institution A						
Institution B						
Institution C						
Credit Union						

Bank or savings and loan #3: _____

	Loan Amount	Number of Payments	Payment Amount	Payment Period	Annual Percentage Rate (APR)	Total Finance Charge (TFC)
Institution A						
Institution B						
Institution C						
Credit Union						

Step B

Loan officer: _____

Interview questions: _____

_____

_____

_____

_____

_____

_____

_____

LAB REPORT

Step C

Use your chart and interview notes to answer the questions below.

1. Which lending institution offers the lowest interest rate?

   _____

2. Which loan allows the lowest monthly payment?

   _____

3. For each loan, determine what percentage of the consumer's take-home pay would be devoted to credit debt. (Don't forget that the consumer already has some credit debt.)

   _____

4. Which loan would you advise the consumer to buy? Explain your answer.

   _____

   _____

   _____

   _____

   _____

   _____

Step D

Using a word processor or a typewriter, write a two-page report on the steps a person should take throughout his or her adult life to establish and maintain good credit. In the report, use the case of the consumer's search for a loan as an example of the need to evaluate all aspects of a loan offer. Also, include references to your interview with the loan officer.

UNIT 6 Insurance

ATTITUDE INVENTORY

Before you begin Unit 6, take stock of your attitudes by completing the following inventory. Read each statement and decide how you feel about it—agree, disagree, or undecided. Write your answers in the blanks.

1. If people are careful, they may avoid all economic risks.

2. People who have a great deal of money do not need insurance.

3. Most people are adequately insured.

4. Renters do not need home and property insurance.

5. The government should provide insurance protection for those who cannot afford it.

6. One insurance company is as good as the next.

7. Insurance policies of any one type are basically the same in terms of cost and features.

8. You can buy insurance on the life of any person.

9. A good driver does not need to waste his or her money on automobile insurance.

10. Automobile insurance protects drivers from responsibility for breaking the law.

11. A doctor is the best person to advise you about the type of medical and health insurance to buy.

12. A teenager does not need to learn about social security because the program is only for old people.

13. If you are not working, one of the things you can do without is life insurance.

14. Most people do not need health insurance because they probably have enough money saved to pay their medical and hospital bills.

15. There is no point to saving money for retirement since social security benefits will provide all you need to live on.

1. _____

2. _____

3. _____

4. _____

5. _____

6. _____

7. _____

8. _____

9. _____

10. _____

11. _____

12. _____

13. _____

14. _____

15. _____

RECHECKING YOUR ATTITUDE

Before going on to the next unit, answer the Attitude Inventory questions a second time. Then compare the two sets of responses. On how many statements have your attitudes changed? Can you account for these shifts in your opinions? What do you know now that you did not know then?

1. If people are careful, they may avoid all economic risks.   1. _____

2. People who have a great deal of money do not need insurance.   2. _____

3. Most people are adequately insured.   3. _____

4. Renters do not need home and property insurance.   4. _____

5. The government should provide insurance protection for those who
   cannot afford it.   5. _____

6. One insurance company is as good as the next.   6. _____

7. Insurance policies of any one type are basically the same in terms of cost
   and features.   7. _____

8. You can buy insurance on the life of any person.   8. _____

9. A good driver does not need to waste his or her money on automobile
   insurance.   9. _____

10. Automobile insurance protects drivers from responsibility for breaking the
    law.   10. _____

11. A doctor is the best person to advise you about the type of medical and
    health insurance to buy.   11. _____

12. A teenager does not need to learn about social security because the
    program is only for old people.   12. _____

13. If you are not working, one of the things you can do without is life
    insurance.   13. _____

14. Most people do not need health insurance because they probably have
    enough money saved to pay their medical and hospital bills.   14. _____

15. There is no point to saving money for retirement since social security
    benefits will provide all you need to live on.   15. _____

Answers changed_____ Why?_____

_____

_____

_____

_____

_____

_____

_____

_____

_____

_____

_____

CHAPTER 18 Property and Home Insurance

REVIEWING CONSUMER TERMS

Pair up with another student and quiz each other on the meaning and definition for each of the following vocabulary terms.

coinsurance clause	personal liability insurance
homeowners policy	personal property
indemnification	physical damage coverage
insurable interest	policy
insurance	premium
medical payments coverage	property insurance

_____

_____

_____

_____

_____

_____

_____

_____

_____

_____

_____

_____

_____

_____

_____

_____

_____

_____

_____

_____

_____

_____

_____

_____

_____

_____

_____

CHAPTER 18 Property and Home Insurance

REVIEWING FACTS AND IDEAS

1. What is the main purpose of insurance?

   _____

   _____

2. What factors should you consider when selecting insurance agents?

   _____

   _____

3. How are risks and losses shared by insurance?

   _____

   _____

   _____

4. What are the three broad categories of risk against which insurance protects?

   _____

   _____

5. What is the importance of insurance to the consumer? to the economy?

   _____

   _____

   _____

   _____

6. What is group insurance and how does it work?

   _____

   _____

   _____

7. What specific risks does a homeowners policy cover?

   _____

   _____

   _____

8. List the factors that determine the cost of property insurance.

   _____

   _____

   _____

CHAPTER 18 *Property and Home Insurance*

APPLICATION ACTIVITY 1

Kim and Paul Takimoto are thinking about some major changes in their insurance coverage. They want to make sure that they are protected for possible losses. They also want to find a new insurance agent. Help with these decisions.

1. Paul has recently purchased a new notebook computer for use when he travels on business. Paul already has a desktop computer in his home office. What type of insurance will cover the notebook computer? Explain.

_____

_____

_____

_____

2. Now that Paul is operating a business from home, he and Kim are concerned about liability for injuries to business visitors. What type of insurance coverage do they need to protect themselves? Explain.

_____

_____

_____

_____

_____

3. Kim and Paul currently have a basic form of homeowners insurance (HO-1). They feel they need more coverage. They recently built a small storage building behind their house. Also, they live in an area with very low temperatures in the winter, so snow, ice, and frozen pipes could be a problem. What form of homeowners policy would you recommend? Explain why.

_____

_____

_____

4. Paul and Kim are looking for an insurance agent. For each situation described below, decide whether you would consider buying insurance from the agent. In each case, briefly explain your choice.

   a. Paul tries calling Agent 1 four times. The first three times he gets a busy signal; the fourth time, an answering service. He leaves a message, but his call is never returned.

_____

_____

_____

_____

b. When Paul calls Agent 2, he gets an answering machine. He leaves a message and early that evening receives a callback. The agent asks Paul a long list of questions about his insurance needs. Then she requests a few days to "get together some possibilities." They agree to meet at Paul's home later that week.

_____

_____

_____

_____

c. Kim got Agent 3 on the phone on the first try. The agent asked several questions about their insurance needs and promises to call back the next day. She does. The premiums she quotes, however, seem high. When Kim inquires about the most cost efficient coverage, Agent 3 responds, "No one can ever have too much insurance."

_____

_____

_____

_____

d. Agent 4 quotes similarly high premiums. When Paul and Kim question the figures, the agent suggests that they are "not familiar with real-world costs these days." When Kim offers some cost cutting suggestions, the agent implies that she does not understand how insurance works. The agent leaves his figures with Paul and Kim and tells them "to get in touch if you're interested."

_____

_____

_____

e. After a brief initial phone contact, Agent 5 meets Paul and Kim for breakfast one morning before work. They do the survey of insurance needs over their meal, and the agent gives them some brochures describing basic coverages. He singles out two dealing with economy plans. The examples, he admits, are not totally accurate for their situation. If they are genuinely interested, however, the agent promises to work up detailed figures. He also describes some features (like flood insurance) that no other agent has mentioned.

_____

_____

_____

5. Paul and Kim know that they need adequate insurance protection, but they must also watch their budget. What suggestions would you make to them about things they can do to lower the cost of their insurance?

_____

_____

_____

_____

_____

CHAPTER 18

Property and Home Insurance

APPLICATION ACTIVITY 2

A. Refer to the different forms of homeowners policies described in your textbook. Then determine the minimum coverage (basic, broad, or comprehensive) needed to protect against the following losses.

Loss	Coverage Required
1. A neighbor's five-year-old son drives the family car through your front-yard fence.	1. _____
2. A tornado levels the house.	2. _____
3. A helicopter crash-lands on your garage.	3. _____
4. Your hot-water tank ruptures, flooding the basement recreation room.	4. _____
5. While you are away one weekend, thieves pull a moving van up to your house and empty it of all furniture, appliances, and personal belongings.	5. _____
6. During a winter storm, the back porch collapses from the weight of accumulated ice and snow.	6. _____
7. A sinkhole mysteriously appears in your backyard and swallows up the toolshed and patio.	7. _____
8. During an earthquake, a hillside slips and demolishes one wing of your house.	8. _____ _____
9. Neighborhood children playing with firecrackers set the roof ablaze.	9. _____
10. An explosion in a manufacturing plant several blocks away shatters every window in your house.	10. _____
11. Subzero temperatures cause the household water pipes to freeze and burst.	11. _____
12. An earthen dam located in the hills above your town gives way, flooding the whole community.	12. _____ _____
13. While rearranging furniture, you accidentally poke a heavy brass floor lamp through a picture window.	13. _____
14. Your chimney collapses, damaging the roof and bringing down the deck awning at the back of the house.	14. _____
15. A lively pajama party at your home brings down the first-floor ceiling, including an expensive lighting fixture in the dining room.	15. _____
16. A neighbor who said he could fix anything suffers a severe shock and burns while trying to repair your electric range.	16. _____

A. Assume you are a home owner who has the insurance coverages summarized in Figure 18-2 in your textbook. Your house is insured for 80 percent of its value. What is the maximum amount you would receive in each of the following situations? Explain how you arrived at each figure.

1. A tornado levels the house. You save nothing.

_____

_____

_____

2. A helicopter crash-lands on your garage, destroying it and your new $16,000 car. Reconstruction will cost $6,000.

_____

_____

_____

3. While you are away one weekend, thieves use a moving van to empty your house. In addition to furniture, appliances, and ordinary personal belongings, you lose two $300 watches and a $1,000 camera.

_____

_____

_____

4. While demonstrating some Fourth of July fireworks, you accidentally set fire to your neighbor's house.

a. The dwelling, valued at $210,000, is totally destroyed. Fortunately no one is hurt. With personal property, however, the loss comes to $285,000.

_____

_____

b. Not only is your neighbor's house destroyed, but one of their children is seriously burned. Medical bills quickly mount to $50,000. Your neighbors file suit for $1 million. This figure is based on the pain, suffering, and disfigurement of their child and is in addition to property damage claims. Eventually the court awards them $300,000.

_____

_____

_____

5. You are painting the exterior of your home.

a. You step back to admire your work and trip over an open toolbox. Follow-up care for the hip injury you suffer eventually costs $3,000.

_____

_____

b. It is the mail carrier who trips over the toolbox. He sues for $50,000 but is eventually awarded only half that amount.

_____

_____

CHAPTER 19 *Automobile Insurance*

REVIEWING CONSUMER TERMS

Break the class into groups of four people to play a game of concentration. As a group, write each of the following terms on 3″ × 3″ cards. Then, write each term on another set of 3″ × 3″ cards. Place all of the cards face down on a table or on the floor. Take turns flipping cards over and trying to match the definitions with the terms.

bodily injury liability coverage

collision coverage

comprehensive physical damage coverage

deductible

financial responsibility laws

medical payments coverage

property damage liability

state automobile insurance plan

uninsured motorists

_____

_____

_____

_____

_____

_____

_____

_____

_____

_____

_____

_____

_____

_____

_____

_____

_____

_____

_____

_____

_____

_____

_____

_____

CHAPTER **19** *Automobile Insurance*

REVIEWING FACTS AND IDEAS

1. Why is car insurance necessary?

   _____

   _____

   _____

   _____

   _____

2. Name six basic kinds of automobile insurance.

   _____

   _____

   _____

   _____

   _____

3. What other types of auto insurance coverage are available?

   _____

   _____

   _____

   _____

   _____

4. What are the factors that determine automobile insurance rates?

   _____

   _____

   _____

   _____

   _____

5. What are two alternative insurance systems?

   _____

   _____

   _____

   _____

   _____

CHAPTER 19 Automobile Insurance

APPLICATION ACTIVITY 1

A. Described below are a number of driving mishaps in which you might be involved. You have insurance. You carry all of the basic coverages—bodily injury, medical payments, uninsured motorists, property damage, comprehensive. and collision. Identify the portion (or portions) of your policy that will pay the costs of each accident. (*Note:* When more than one coverage is involved, specify which will pay what.)

1. You park your car on a hill but forget to curb your wheels. While you are away, the brakes fail. Your car rolls down the hill, flattens a fence, demolishes a porch, and finally comes to a rest inside someone's dining room. Your car suffers minor damage but the fence, porch, and dining room wall are total losses.

_____

_____

2. Your next-door neighbor knocks a potted plant off her balcony. The plant hits your car, shattering the windshield.

_____

3. While riding your bicycle past a construction site, you are sideswiped by a car and thrown into a ditch. The driver who hit you flees the scene and is not caught. You suffer a broken arm and a severe concussion and are hospitalized for eight days.

_____

_____

4. While turning into the school parking lot, you stop suddenly to avoid a pedestrian and are hit by the car behind you. You are unhurt, but your car's gas tank is punctured, and the fire department must be called. The student driving the other car has no insurance.

_____

_____

5. You are late for work. You speed around a corner at a blind intersection and run into a moving van parked in the street. Your car gets the greater damage (the van is barely dented.) The impact of the collision, however, topples some of the van's contents. Several items are broken, and one of the movers suffers two cracked ribs.

_____

_____

6. Your mother is driving you to school. At a major intersection, another car runs a red light and hits you broadside. The other driver is insured. As a result of the accident, your mother suffers numerous cuts and bruises and is bedridden for several days. You appear all right. Six months later, however, you begin having back pains. Your doctor tells you that the accident is indirectly responsible.

_____

_____

_____

_____

B. Review text pages 294 and 300. Then do the problems below.

1. Mario liked to drive and weave and speed in and out of traffic. One day the traffic stopped and Mario didn't. He slammed into a brand new Corvette, totalling the car and severely injuring its occupants, Sam and Mary. Bad as the accident was, Mario was not concerned. His injuries were minor and his insurance, he was sure, would pay for everything. Was he right? (Note: Mario carried 15/30/15 coverage, the state minimum. Damages were assessed as shown below, and Mario was held fully responsible.) Who paid what? Complete the chart.

	Limit		Court Award		Insurance Pays	Mario Pays
B.I.	_____	per person	Sam	$50,000	_____	_____
	_____	per accident	Mary	$10,000	_____	_____
P.D.	_____	per accident	Sam	$25,000	_____	_____
TOTAL				$85,000	_____	_____

2. Suppose Mario's policy limits had been 50/100/50. Would it have made any difference in his personal liability? To find out, complete the chart.

	Limit		Court Award		Insurance Pays	Mario Pays
B.I.	_____	per person	Sam	$50,000	_____	_____
	_____	per accident	Mary	$10,000	_____	_____
P.D.	_____	per accident	Sam	$25,000	_____	_____

3. Assume that Mario's hitting the Corvette caused a chain reaction as follows: Corvette (brand-new) hits Mustang (almost new) hits Pacer (somewhat old) hits pedestrian (in crosswalk). Pedestrian sues Pacer, Pacer sues Mustang, Mustang sues Corvette, and everyone sues Mario. The court awards damages in the amounts shown below. Mario's coverage limits are 100/300/100. Must he pay any of the accident victims out of his own pocket? Complete the chart.

		Limit	Court Award		Insurance Pays	Mario Pays
B.I.	_____ per person		Corvette: Sam	$50,000	_____	_____
			Mary	$10,000	_____	_____
	_____ per accident		Mustang: Driver	$8,000	_____	_____
			Pacer: Driver	—	_____	_____
			Passenger	$3,000	_____	_____
			Pedestrian	$150,000	_____	_____
P.D.	_____ per accident		Corvette	$25,000	_____	_____
			Mustang	$4,000	_____	_____
			Pacer	$850	_____	_____
	TOTAL			$250,850	_____	_____

CHAPTER 19 Automobile Insurance

APPLICATION ACTIVITY 2

When parents add teenage drivers to an auto insurance policy, it can mean hundreds or even thousands of dollars more in premiums. Why? Study the table below to find out.

ACCIDENTS BY AGE OF DRIVERS, 1993						
Age Group	Number of drivers	% of total	Drivers in fatal accidents	% of total	Drivers in all accidents	% of total
Under 20	8,889,000	5.1	6,400	11.8	2,780,000	13.2
20–24	16,875,000	9.6	8,100	15.1	3,210,000	15.2
25–34	40,423,000	23.0	13,500	25.0	5,500,000	26.1
35–44	38,650,000	22.0	10,400	19.3	4,160,000	19.7
45–54	27,026,000	15.4	5,900	10.9	2,380,000	11.3
55–64	19,494,000	11.1	3,800	7.1	1,420,000	6.7
65–74	16,861,000	9.6	3,000	5.6	1,030,000	4.9
Over 74	7,661,000	4.4	2,800	5.2	620,000	2.9
Totals	**175,878,000**	**100.0**	53,900	**100.0**	21,100,000	**100.0**

Source: National Safety Council.

1. Note the makeup of the total driving population.

   a. Which age group had the highest number of drivers?

   _____

   b. Which age group had the lowest number of drivers?

   _____

2. Compare the accident statistics to these figures.

   a. Which age group had the highest percentage of accidents?

   _____

   b. Which age group had the highest percentage of fatal accidents?

   _____

   c. Which age group had the lowest percentage of accidents?

   _____

   d. Which age group had the lowest percentage of fatal accidents?

   _____

   e. Are those the results you would expect, given the breakdown of the driving population in the table (question 1)? Explain.

   _____

   _____

   _____

   _____

   _____

   _____

3. Assume that you work for an insurance company. It is your job to set premium rates.

   a. For which age group would you set the highest premiums? Why? (Use the data in the table to support your decision.)

_____

_____

_____

_____

_____

   b. For which age group would you set the lowest premiums? Why? (Again, use the data in the table to support your decision.)

_____

_____

_____

_____

_____

_____

CHAPTER **20** *Life and Health Insurance*

REVIEWING CONSUMER TERMS

Use each of the following terms in a paper about life and health insurance.

cash value
health maintenance organization (HMO)
major medical expense coverage
managed care
Medicaid

Medicare
permanent insurance
term insurance
whole-life policy
workers' compensation

_____

_____

_____

_____

_____

_____

_____

_____

_____

_____

_____

_____

_____

_____

_____

_____

_____

_____

_____

_____

_____

_____

_____

_____

_____

_____

_____

_____

CHAPTER **20** *Life and Health Insurance*

REVIEWING FACTS AND IDEAS

1. Explain the difference between term life insurance and permanent life insurance.

   _____

   _____

   _____

   _____

   _____

2. Name three factors to consider when buying life insurance.

   _____

   _____

   _____

   _____

   _____

3. What are the three kinds of health insurance that make up basic coverage?

   _____

   _____

   _____

   _____

   _____

   _____

4. Name some government health insurance programs and describe how they work.

   _____

   _____

   _____

   _____

   _____

   _____

5. What are the two goals of a managed care plan?

   _____

   _____

   _____

   _____

   _____

CHAPTER **20** *Life and Health Insurance*

APPLICATION ACTIVITY 1

Assume you are an insurance agent. You have been called to the apartment residence of Tom and Marina Goralski. The Goralskis are both twenty-seven and have been married for five years. Marina is a loan officer with Conestoga Savings, a local bank. (She earns $2,500 a month.) Tom is a writer who works at home and cares for their two-year-old son. He earns around $20,000 a year. Tom and Marina are about to take a big step financially. After five years of saving for a down payment, they are ready to buy their own home (total cost—$90,000). With their growing family and this expensive new investment, Tom and Marina think they should reevaluate their life insurance coverage. At present, Tom has a $10,000 whole-life policy from Mutual of Anystate. (His parents bought the policy for him when he was in high school, but he now pays the premiums himself.) Marina has term life insurance through her group plan at work, but she would lose that coverage if she were laid off or changed jobs.

1. In general terms, what would you advise Tom and Marina to do about their personal life insurance coverage? Why?

   _____

   _____

   _____

   _____

2. What further information about whole-life policies would be helpful to you in advising Tom and Marina? Explain.

   _____

   _____

   _____

   _____

   _____

3. Do you think it is necessary for both Marina and Tom to have life insurance? Explain your reasons.

   _____

   _____

   _____

   _____

   _____

4. What other types of life insurance might you suggest to Marina and Tom? (List at least two and explain why you would recommend them.)

   _____

   _____

   _____

   _____

   _____

5. Assume that Tom decides to purchase more insurance, namely a term policy in the amount of $50,000. Fill out the application for him. You are recommending the following clauses: (a) waiver of premiums, (b) automatic premium loan, and (c) assignment. Tom wishes to pay the premiums in quarterly installments and wants any dividends to be used for premium reduction. He gives you a $75 check for the first premium.

PART 1 OF APPLICATION FOR INSURANCE

1. Full name of applicant USE BLACK INK ONLY

8. Date of Birth	Month	Day	Year	AGE LAST BIRTHDAY

2. A. Residence: Street

City or Town

County   State

B. Residence addresses (ST., CITY AND STATE) last three years

C. Do you contemplate a change in residence or foreign travel?
IF SO, GIVE DETAILS

9. Birthplace
CITY, STATE

10. Are you
CHECK ☐ Single ☐ Married ☐ Widowed ☐ Divorced

11. During the past five years have you had advice, attendance, or treatment by a physician or any other person? If so, give nature of ailment, duration, approximate date and names and addresses of physicians or other persons consulted.

3. A. Occupation

B. Name of employer and business address

C. Previous occupation in last five years

D. Have you any other occupations? IF SO, GIVE DETAILS

E. Do you contemplate any change in occupation?
IF SO, GIVE DETAILS

12. A. Plan of insurance

CHECK PROVISIONS DESIRED
Waiver of   Waiver of Premiums   Death by Acci-
B. ☐ Premiums C. ☐ and Monthly Income D. ☐ dental Means

13. Amount of insurance

4. A. Have you ever piloted or have you any intention of piloting any type of aircraft?

B. Have you taken any aerial flight in the last 12 months other than as a passenrer?
IF EITHER PART IS ANSWERED "YES," SUBMIT AVIATION SUPPLEMENT

14. Premiums payable in advance CHECK METHOD OF PAYMENT
☐ Annually ☐ Semiannually ☐ Quarterly ☐ Monthly

15. Beneficiary GIVEN NAME AND RELATIONSHIP

5. Will insurance now being applied for replace insurance in this or any other company? IF SO, GIVE DETAILS

(Endowments are made payable to the insured at maturity unless otherwise requested.)

6. Are you insured in this Company?

7. Is your life insured in any other company or companies?
IF SO, GIVE FULL DETAILS BELOW

Names of Companies	Amounts	Kinds	Dates of Issue	Special Provisions Waiver	Dis. Inc.	A.D.B.

16. Which of the following rights do you reserve as to a change of beneficiary, any change being subject to the consent of the Company?
STRIKE OUT ONE
A. The right to change and successively change to any beneficiary
B. No right to change except with the consent of all beneficiaries

17. Dividends to be: STRIKE OUT METHODS NOT DESIRED
A. Paid in cash
B. Applied in reduction of premium
C. Used to purchase paid-up additions
D. Left with the Company to accumulate at interest

B. What would be the amount of your disability income, if disabled? EXCLUSIVE OF INSURANCE IN THIS COMPANY

FROM 1. All life insurance policies $ per month
FROM 2. All accident and health policies $ per month

18. Is the Automatic Premium Loan Provision requested?   CHECK ☐ YES ☐ NO

19. Has the first premium on the insurance If so, state amount paid hereby applied for been paid? $

I understand and agree that:

1. If the premium on the insurance herein applied for has been paid to the Company's agent, in exchange for the Company's signed advance premium receipt numbered the same as Part 1 hereof, the insurance as provided by the policy shall be effective from the date of Part 2 of this application PROVIDED the Company shall approve this application at its Home Office. If this application is not so approved, I will accept the return of the premium paid and surrender the advance premium receipt.

2. If the premium on the insurance herein applied for has not been paid, such insurance shall become effective on the date of issue stated in the policy PROVIDED the Company has approved this application at its Home Office, the premium has been paid, and the policy delivered to me while I am in good health.

I hereby declare that all the answers and statements herein contained are full, complete, and true, and have been correctly recorded.

Signed at _____
                City   State
and dated this_____ day of_____ , 19 _____

In My Presence_____

General Agent
submitting application

Applicant _____
Address all
mail to _____

Agent who actually
solicited this application

CHAPTER **20** *Life and Health Insurance*

APPLICATION ACTIVITY 2

A. For years, health care costs have outpaced inflation. Even when the overall inflation rate has been in double digits (10 and 12 percent), medical costs have risen faster. The chart below illustrates this trend. It shows the change in the cost of one surgical procedure over the thirty-year period from 1965 to 1995.

Year	Cost (in dollars)	Amount of Increase (in dollars)	Percentage Increase
1965	839		
1970	1,397		
1975	2,208		
1980	3,533		
1985	5,299		
1990	7,843		
1995	11,921		

1. Complete the chart. Compute the actual increased cost in dollars for each five-year period. Then use that figure to determine the percentage increase.

2. Analyze the trend of operation charges for each decade.

   a. From 1965 to 1975, what was the average percentage increase in cost?　　　a. _____

   b. From 1975 to 1985, what was the average percentage increase in cost?　　　b. _____

   c. From 1985 to 1995, what was the average percentage increase in cost?　　　c. _____

   d. What trend do these figures establish?

   _____

   _____

   _____

   _____

3. Summarize the increases for the entire three-decade period.

   a. What was the total increase in cost from 1965 to 1995?　　　a. _____

   b. What percentage increase does this figure represent?　　　b. _____

   c. What was the average percentage increase per year?　　　c. _____

4. If you were an insurance agent, how would you use these figures to sell health insurance?

   _____

   _____

   _____

   _____

B. For each case below, identify the type (or types) of health insurance coverage that would best meet the needs of the persons described.

1. Denny Jordan, a forward on the varsity football team, injures his back in a scrimmage. He is hospitalized for three weeks. No surgery is necessary, but Denny spends much of his time in traction. He is completely helpless and requires round-the-clock nursing care.

   _____

   _____

   _____

   _____

2. Tracy Weiss is the buyer for the shoe department of a large women's specialty store. She feels the store's group health plan is more than adequate to meet ordinary medical expenses. She is less satisfied with its provisions for long-term illness (there is a lifetime limit of $60,000 on payments). She decides to buy additional coverage on her own.

   _____

   _____

3. Lisa Carretino is eight. When a "tummyache" turns into appendicitis, she is rushed to the hospital for emergency surgery. The operation goes well, but Lisa spends five days in the children's ward before her doctor allows her to go home.

   _____

   _____

4. Michael loves the taste of the jawbreakers inside old-fashioned gumball machines. He buys a few and ends up with a broken tooth, which has to be fitted with a cap.

   _____

   _____

5. Gwendolyn Miller is sixty-seven and suffers from advanced heart disease. Her doctor recommends bypass surgery. Gwendolyn is concerned because she knows the procedure is expensive ($10,000 excluding follow-up care).

   _____

   _____

   _____

6. Rupert Kelsey is a carpenter. He frames buildings for a major construction company. One day Rupert slips on the job and falls two stories, breaking his right leg near the hip. The fracture does not heal well. There are complications. Rupert undergoes surgery on three separate occasions and eventually spends nearly two years in a cast.

   _____

   _____

   _____

   _____

CHAPTER 21 *Income Insurance*

REVIEWING CONSUMER TERMS

Use each of the following terms in a paragraph to demonstrate you know its meaning.

annuity

disability benefits

old-age benefits

social security number

social security program

Supplemental Security Income (SSI)

survivors' benefits

unemployment insurance

_____

_____

_____

_____

_____

_____

_____

_____

_____

_____

_____

_____

_____

_____

_____

_____

_____

_____

_____

_____

_____

_____

_____

_____

_____

_____

_____

_____

_____

_____

_____

_____

CHAPTER 21 *Income Insurance*

REVIEWING FACTS AND IDEAS

1. Name three problems that existed during the Depression which prompted passage of the Social Security Act.

_____

_____

_____

_____

_____

2. List five benefits offered by social security.

_____

_____

_____

_____

_____

3. Who pays for social security?

_____

_____

_____

_____

4. What is disability income insurance and how does it work?

_____

_____

_____

_____

5. What is the difference between a pension and an annuity?

_____

_____

_____

_____

CHAPTER **21** *Income Insurance*

APPLICATION ACTIVITY 1

The graph below shows the projected (or predicted) income and expenditures of the Social Security Trust Fund from 1990 to 2050. Study the graph carefully. Then use the questions that follow to analyze its content.

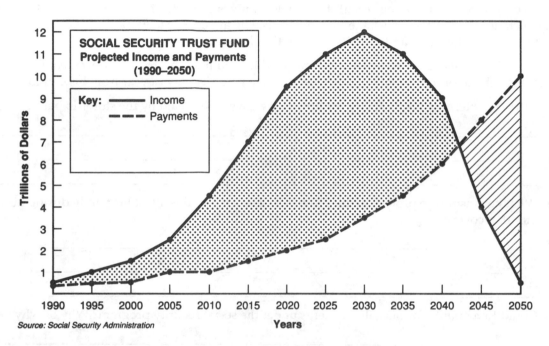

1. Over what period of time is trust fund income expected to exceed payments? What is the trend for payments during this same time period?

   _____

   _____

   _____

2. In 1990 trust fund income and payments were just about equal. When is this next expected to occur? What graph characteristics did you use to reach this conclusion?

   _____

   _____

   _____

3. The graph shows what will happen to social security income and expenditures if no changes are made in the system. What kinds of changes do you think might eliminate or reduce the striped area in the graph?

   _____

   _____

   _____

CHAPTER  21 *Income Insurance*

APPLICATION ACTIVITY 2

Ken Anderson manages a sports equipment store. He has worked for the same company for five years, and his current take-home pay is about $2,100 a month. Ken and his wife have two children, ages three and one. The Andersons rent a two-bedroom apartment and have six payments left on their car. They both carry life insurance ($10,000 coverage each). The whole family is protected by the health plan Ken pays into at work, which does not include coverage for employees who are unable to work. Given their current needs and responsibilities, Ken and his wife feel that they have enough insurance.

1. Ken is painting his house when he falls from a ladder and hurts his back. The accident leaves him totally disabled for four months. (Note: Ken has five paid sick days a year from his employer.)

   a. During the term of his disability, for how many days is Ken paid by the store? Explain.

   _____

   _____

   _____

   b. What key insurance protection does Ken lack? How might this affect his family during his four-month recovery?

   _____

   _____

   _____

   c. Could Ken qualify for disability benefits under the social security program? Why or why not?

   _____

   _____

   _____

2. Assume that Ken and other store employees also pay into a disability insurance plan. Benefits are paid after a waiting period of thirty days. They are limited to 60 percent of employee wages up to a maximum of $1,200 per month. Benefits are paid monthly until the disabled employee either returns to work or reaches retirement age.

   a. During the term of his disability, for how many days is Ken paid? Explain.

   _____

   _____

   _____

   b. How much does Ken receive monthly in disability income? Show your calculations.

   _____

   _____

   _____

   c. Does this coverage change your evaluation of Ken's family situation (1b above)? In what ways?

   _____

   _____

UNIT **6** *LAB Insurance*

RESEARCHING THE BENEFITS OF INSURANCE

Unit 6 presents the advantages of having insurance. In this lab, you will have the opportunity to talk directly with those who provide insurance and those who receive the benefits of it.

TOOLS

1. News magazines and newspapers
2. Financial and consumer magazines
3. Literature from insurance providers and the Social Security Administration
4. History and economics textbooks

PROCEDURES

Read the lab in your textbook and complete each activity using the space provided below.

Step A

Interview questions: _____

_____

_____

_____

_____

_____

_____

_____

_____

_____

Step B

Worker #1: _____

Telephone number: _____

Worker #2: _____

Telephone number: _____

Worker #3: _____

Telephone number: _____

Step C

Interview questions: _____

_____

_____

_____

_____

_____

_____

_____

_____

_____

_____

_____

Step D

Employee #1: _____

Telephone number: _____

Employee #2: _____

Telephone number: _____

Employee #3: _____

Telephone number: _____

LAB REPORT
Step E

Use your notes from the six interviews to answer the questions below.

1. What was the average percentage of income the three workers devoted to insurance premiums?

   _____

2. How did the cost of premiums, deductibles, and coinsurance payments affect the workers' satisfaction with their health insurance?

   _____

3. What was the average cost per employee for a company to provide health and/or life insurance?

   _____

4. What was the average cost of social security taxes to the three employers?

   _____

5. How have the employers attempted to deal with the cost of providing employee insurance benefits?

   _____

Step F

Using a word processor or a typewriter, write a two-page report on the economic advantages and disadvantages of life, health, and income insurance for the employee, the employer, and U.S. taxpayers.

UNIT 7 Transportation and Travel

ATTITUDE INVENTORY

Before you begin Unit 7, take stock of your attitudes by completing the following inventory. Read each statement and decide how you feel about it—agree, disagree, or undecided. Write your answers in the blanks.

1. An automobile is a necessity for the modern consumer.

   1. _____

2. The cheapest way to travel is always by car.

   2. _____

3. Widespread ownership of automobiles presents social problems in many communities.

   3. _____

4. The most powerful car is, in the long run, the best car for most consumers.

   4. _____

5. Today many Americans have more time for recreation than did their parents and grandparents.

   5. _____

6. A consumer who cannot pay cash for a car should not buy one.

   6. _____

7. The small-car buyer will need more optional equipment than the buyer of a larger automobile.

   7. _____

8. Results of road tests reported by various magazines are of real value to the consumer.

   8. _____

9. Dealer reputation is usually more important than the price of a car.

   9. _____

10. Miles-per-gallon ratings published by the Environmental Protection Agency are more reliable than the experiences of automobile sales people.

    10. _____

11. "Leave your credit card at home" is poor advice for a vacationer.

    11. _____

12. The used-car buyer always "buys somebody else's problem."

    12. _____

13. Warranties are always one of the most important points for consumers to consider before buying a used car.

    13. _____

14. Travel agents cannot do anything for you that you cannot do better and more cheaply for yourself.

    14. _____

15. Budget motels are suitable only for those who like to "rough it."

    15. _____

16. Public transportation is for poor people only.

    16. _____

RECHECKING YOUR ATTITUDE

Before going on to the next unit, answer the Attitude Inventory questions a second time. Then compare the two sets of responses. On how many statements have your attitudes changed? Can you account for these shifts in your opinions? What do you know now that you did not know then?

1. An automobile is a necessity for the modern consumer.

1. _____

2. The cheapest way to travel is always by car.

2. _____

3. Widespread ownership of automobiles presents social problems in many communities.

3. _____

4. The most powerful car is, in the long run, the best car for most consumers.

4. _____

5. Today many Americans have more time for recreation than did their parents and grandparents.

5. _____

6. A consumer who cannot pay cash for a car should not buy one.

6. _____

7. The small-car buyer will need more optional equipment than the buyer of a larger automobile.

7. _____

8. Results of road tests reported by various magazines are of real value to the consumer.

8. _____

9. Dealer reputation is usually more important than the price of a car.

9. _____

10. Miles-per-gallon ratings published by the Environmental Protection Agency are more reliable than the experiences of automobile sales people.

10. _____

11. "Leave your credit card at home" is poor advice for a vacationer.

11. _____

12. The used-car buyer always "buys somebody else's problem."

12. _____

13. Warranties are always one of the most important points for consumers to consider before buying a used car.

13. _____

14. Travel agents cannot do anything for you that you cannot do better and more cheaply for yourself.

14. _____

15. Budget motels are suitable only for those who like to "rough it."

15. _____

16. Public transportation is for poor people only.

16. _____

Answers changed _____ Why? _____

_____

_____

_____

_____

_____

_____

_____

_____

_____

_____

_____

CHAPTER 22 *Buying or Leasing a New or Used Car*

REVIEWING CONSUMER TERMS

Use each of the following terms in an essay about buying new and used cars.

depreciation

diagnostic center

odometer

options

standard equipment

sticker price

tire tread

warranty

_____

_____

_____

_____

_____

_____

_____

_____

_____

_____

_____

_____

_____

_____

_____

_____

_____

_____

_____

_____

_____

_____

_____

_____

_____

CHAPTER 22 — Buying or Leasing a New or Used Car

REVIEWING FACTS AND IDEAS

1. Name four advantages and four disadvantages in buying a new car.

_____
_____
_____
_____

2. Describe the seven major car sizes and types.

_____
_____
_____

3. What percentage of disposable income is the average amount spent on owning and operating a car?

_____
_____
_____
_____

4. What steps should be followed in making an on-lot inspection of a used car?

_____
_____
_____
_____

5. Suggest two sources of help in evaluating a used car.

_____
_____
_____
_____

6. Describe the differences between an open-end lease and a closed-end lease.

_____
_____
_____
_____

CHAPTER **22** Buying or Leasing a New or Used car

APPLICATION ACTIVITY 1

Assume that you are in the market for a new car. Before you spend your money, take time to think about the kind of automobile you really need. The questions below can help you. Place your answers in the student column. Then ask two other people the same questions and record their answers in the remaining columns.

Automotive Needs	Student	Parent	Other Adult
1. How many miles per week will you be driving?			
2. Will most of your driving be on (a) city streets, (b) country roads, (c) limited-access highways, or (d) a combination of these?			
3. How many cars are there in your family now?			
4. How many people must your car hold?			
5. How much money do you have budgeted for purchase of your car?			
6. Do you prefer the look, handling, and conveniences of (a) a compact, (b) a subcompact, (c) a mid-sized, or (d) a full-sized car?			
7. Which of the following options do you consider necessary: (a) automatic transmission, (b) air conditioning, (c) AM/FM radio, (d) power brakes, (e) power steering, (f) sun roof, (g) vinyl roof, (h) bucket seats? List any others.			
8. Can you do any vehicle maintenance yourself, or will you have to pay for the services of a professional mechanic?			
9. Do you see a car as (a) basic transportation, (b) an expression of your personality, or (c) both?			
10. Will your car be used to pull a trailer, camper, or boat? Which?			
11. Will your car ever have to haul large pieces of furniture or other heavy loads?			
12. How long do you plan to have this car before replacing it with a new model?			

Adapted from America on Wheels, Activity Master 12--"The Best Car for You," courtesy of Motor Vehicle Manufacturers Association of the United States, Inc.

How do your answers compare with those of the two people you questioned? What do you think accounts for this result?

_____

_____

CHAPTER 22   Buying or Leasing a New or Used Car

APPLICATION ACTIVITY 2

Most drivers are not aware of the true cost of owning a car. This fact is easy to understand. Vehicle expenses accumulate weekly or monthly, but few drivers bother to total them on an annual basis. The government, however, publishes such data to help new-car buyers. The chart below is an example. Use it to answer the questions that follow, keeping in mind that the figures should be updated each year. The figures in the table also assume that a car will be used for 12 years.

Size	Depreciation	Insurance	Maintenance	Parking & Tolls	Tires	Finance Charges	License, Registration and Taxes	Fuel & Oil Excluding Taxes	Fuel & Oil Taxes	Total Cost
Subcompact	8.6	7.1	4.0	1.3	0.7	1.6	0.8	3.5	1.3	
Compact	8.7	7.0	3.9	1.3	0.9	1.6	0.7	4.0	1.4	
Mid-sized Car	10.7	7.0	4.2	1.3	1.0	2.0	0.9	4.6	1.7	
Full-sized Car	13.5	7.2	4.5	1.3	1.0	2.5	1.1	5.0	1.8	
Full-sized Van	14.2	8.5	4.2	1.3	1.4	2.9	1.2	8.1	3.0	

Suburban-Based Operation (cents per mile)

Source: U.S. Department of Transportation

1. What is the total cost per mile for each type of vehicle? Add together the nine items covered by the chart and place your totals in the last column.

2. Study the figures for fuel and oil costs. How do they seem to be related to vehicle size?

_____

3. What percentage of total cost does insurance represent for each of the following types of cars?

Full-sized models _____   Compacts _____   Subcompacts _____

4. Based on the percentages in question 3, what seems to be the relationship between car size and insurance costs? Why do you think this is so?

_____

_____

5. How does depreciation rank when compared with other vehicle costs?

_____

CHAPTER **23** *Owning a Car*

REVIEWING CONSUMER TERMS

Use each of the following terms in a sentence that demonstrates you know its meaning.

full warranty
lemon laws
limited warranty
maintenance schedule
title

_____

_____

_____

_____

_____

_____

_____

_____

_____

_____

_____

_____

_____

_____

_____

_____

_____

_____

_____

_____

_____

_____

_____

_____

_____

_____

_____

_____

_____

_____

_____

_____

_____

CHAPTER **23** *Owning a Car*

REVIEWING FACTS AND IDEAS

1. Name three loan sources for buying a car.

   _____

   _____

   _____

   _____

2. Describe the difference between a full warranty and a limited warranty.

   _____

   _____

   _____

   _____

   _____

   _____

3. In deciding how much you can afford as a down payment on a car, what factors must you consider?

   _____

   _____

   _____

   _____

   _____

   _____

4. What items are usually included in a maintenance schedule?

   _____

   _____

   _____

   _____

   _____

   _____

5. Identify some of the fluid levels that you would check as part of routine vehicle maintenance.

   _____

   _____

   _____

   _____

CHAPTER 23 Owning a Car

APPLICATION ACTIVITY 1

There are many hidden costs involved in owning a car: option charges (usually negotiable with the dealer), finance charges, and, of course, depreciation. Choose a new car that you would like to own and itemize these costs for yourself.

VEHICLE DESCRIPTION AND COST

Year_____ Make_____ Model_____

Body style_____

Standard Features:

_____ _____ _____

_____ _____ _____

_____ _____ _____

Retail price (with standard equipment)............... $_____ a

Options Desired:

_____ $_____

_____ $_____

_____ $_____

_____ $_____

_____ $_____

_____ $_____

(plus) Total cost of options......................... $_____ b

Additional Charges:

Sales tax (_____%) $_____

License fees* $_____

Dealer Preparation** $_____

(plus) Total additional charges...................... $_____ c

(equals) TOTAL PRICE OF CAR.......................... $_____ d

* Amount varies. Assume $200 if no figure is available.

** Only if not included in retail price. If no figure is available, use $250.

FINANCING

Amount to be Financed:

Total price of car.. $_____ e

(minus) Trade-in or down payment...................... $_____ f

(equals) TOTAL AMOUNT TO BE FINANCED.................. $_____ g

Monthly Payment:

Payment plan term (Choose one.)

_____ 24 months (.049)   _____ 42 months (.032)

_____ 30 months (.042)   _____ 48 months (.029)

_____ 36 months (.035)

Amount financed... $_____ h

(times) Payment plan decimal........................ ×_____ i

(equals) MONTHLY PAYMENT............................ $_____ j

Cost of Credit:

Monthly payment... $_____ k

(times) Months in payment plan...................... ×_____ l

(equals) TOTAL INSTALLMENT PRICE..................... $_____ m

(minus) Total amount financed....................... −_____ n

(equals) TOTAL COST OF CREDIT....................... $_____ o

The mere fact that a car has been "preowned" reduces its value. As one dealer explains, "The minute you drive it off my lot, that new car depreciates 15 percent." Such thinking is bad news for new-car buyers, especially those who total their vehicles in accidents or lose them to theft in the first few months of ownership. It is good news, however, for people in the market for used cars. These individuals can apply a depreciation formula to evaluate vehicle prices. To verify this fact, complete the following chart. Assume a purchase price of $14,000. Apply the formula *purchase price × cumulative depreciation rate = total depreciation*.

NEW-CAR DEPRECIATION

Year of Ownership	Approximate Depreciation Rate (percent)	Cumulative Depreciation Rate (total percent)	Total Depreciation (in dollars)
First	33 1/3		
Second	20		
Third	16-2/3		

CHAPTER 23 Owning a Car

APPLICATION ACTIVITY 2

The cost of owning a car goes beyond just its purchase price. When planning which car to buy, you also need to plan the costs of operating and insuring the car. For example, insurance companies often charge higher premiums for sports cars that have a history of higher accidents and/or repair. Using the car you chose in Application Activity 1, calculate the cost of insuring and operating the car.

1. If you were buying a car today, you would most likely buy insurance through your parents' policy. To make a comparison of costs, ask about buying insurance on your own as well as on your family's policy. Call your family's auto insurance agent to get information about the cost of insurance and record the responses below.

   a. What is the annual premium for the car you want to buy if you are not on the family policy?

   _____

   b. What is the annual premium for the car you want to buy if you are on the family policy?

   _____

   c. Does the insurance company allow monthly payments? If so, how much would the monthly payment be in each situation above?

   Payment for a: _____

   Payment for b: _____

   d. What restrictions apply to you as a teenage driver?

   _____

   _____

   _____

   e. Ask the agent about rates for different models of cars. If you chose a different model, could you save money on insurance premiums?

   _____

   _____

   _____

   f. How do the options you chose in Activity 1 affect your insurance premiums? For example, how much money do you save if the car you chose has the following features?

   Antilock brakes: _____

   Airbags: _____

   Alarm system: _____

   g. Are there options you chose that will cost you more money to insure (for example, deluxe wheel covers)? List the options below, then ask the agent the additional cost.

   _____

   _____

   _____

2. Paying for gasoline and regular maintenance are also a part of the cost of owning a car. Research the following questions and record the answers in the space provided.

a. Does the car you chose require premium or regular gasoline? What is the typical price of a gallon of this gasoline?

_____

b. If you plan to buy your car at a dealership, how much does the dealer charge for an oil/filter change?

_____

c. If you plan to have the oil changed at an independent service maintenance facility, how much will an oil/filter change cost?

_____

d. How frequently will your car need to have regular maintenance performed? How much does the dealer charge for this maintenance?

_____

e. If you have the same maintenance done by an independent service facility, what will it cost?

_____

f. How much are the fees for licensing your car? Call the Bureau of Motor Vehicles in your state for information. Include the cost of a driver's license plus your license plates.

_____

g. What is the annual cost of renewing your license plates?

_____

h. Use the space below to calculate the total costs of insuring and operating your car for the first year and to calculate a monthly cost.

	Annually	Monthly
Insurance costs	_____	_____
Gasoline costs (estimated number of miles driven per year times cost per gallon of gasoline)	_____	_____
Oil changes (number of changes times cost per change in a year)	_____	_____
Maintenance	_____	_____
Driver's license	_____	_____
License plates	_____	_____
TOTALS	_____	_____

CHAPTER 24 — Choosing Other Forms of Transportation

REVIEWING CONSUMER TERMS

Use each of the following terms in a paragraph to demonstrate you know its meaning.

American Plan
bus lane
exhaust emissions

package tour
rationing
youth hostel

_____

_____

_____

_____

_____

_____

_____

_____

_____

_____

_____

_____

_____

_____

_____

_____

_____

_____

_____

_____

_____

_____

_____

_____

_____

_____

_____

_____

_____

_____

CHAPTER 24 Choosing Other Forms of Transportation

REVIEWING FACTS AND IDEAS

1. List three advantages to individuals who use mass transit and three advantages to their communities.

    _____

    _____

    _____

2. Describe why some consumers resist using public transportation.

    _____

    _____

    _____

3. What measures have been taken to encourage use of public transportation?

    _____

    _____

    _____

4. Explain ways to choose a vacation site.

    _____

    _____

    _____

    _____

5. Describe the advantages and disadvantages of traveling by bus, train, plane, or private vehicle.

    _____

    _____

    _____

    _____

    _____

    _____

    _____

    _____

6. What facilities are usually available in youth hostels?

    _____

    _____

    _____

CHAPTER 24 Choosing Other Forms of Transportation

APPLICATION ACTIVITY 1

A. Study the table below, then answer the questions that follow it. Data in the table is approximate and percentages may not add to 100 because of rounding.

HOW AMERICANS GET TO WORK

Means of Transportation	1990 Census Percentage	1980 Census Percentage
Workers 16 years old and over	100.0	100.0
Car, truck, or van:	86.5	84.1
Drove alone	73.2	64.4
Carpool	13.4	19.7
Public transportation	5.3	6.4
Motorcycle	0.2	0.4
Bicycle	0.4	0.5
Walked	3.9	5.6
Other means	0.7	0.7
Worked at home	3.0	2.3

Source: U.S. Bureau of the Census.

1. The 1990 census showed 115,070,000 workers. Use this figure and the percentages in the table for the 1990 census to calculate the number of people in each category that follows:

   a. Carpooled to get to work _____

   b. Used public transportation to get to work _____

   c. Worked at home _____

2. What do the differences between the 1980 and 1990 census percentages show with respect to each of the following?

   a. Use of public transportation by workers

   _____

   b. Walking to work

   _____

   c. Workers who drive to work alone

   _____

3. What conclusions might you draw about the future of public transportation?

   _____

   _____

   _____

B. Assume that the annual cost of operating the transit system of Center City is $412.7 million. Assume further that the transit system has 14,000 employees.

1. If revenue from passengers amounts to $174.6 million, how much of the operating budget must be subsidized by taxpayers?

1. _____

2. What percentage of the total budget is met by revenue?

2. _____

3. If federal and state governments contribute $20.4 million to the system, how much of the operating budget must be met by local government?

3. _____

4. If transit employees earn a total of $278 million each year, what is their average annual wage?

4. _____

5. For each of the Center City residents listed in the table below, compute the extra cost of driving to work each day instead of taking the bus.

Resident	Cost of Driving					
	Miles Traveled One Way	Auto Cost per Mile (¢)	Daily Parking Cost ($)	Total Driving Cost ($)	One-Way Bus Fare ($)	Difference ($)
Kurtz	5	26.3	5		.95	
Desiderio	8	23.5	2		.75	
Loomis	15	25.8	7		1.65	
Frankel	24	27.8	8		2.25	

6. Many communities make special transportation arrangements for those who physically cannot drive a car. Often these arrangements include a dial-a-ride service using vans equipped with lifts. Because of the special vehicles, the lack of planned routes, and the time required to help passengers board, such a service is expensive to operate. Consider the figures at the right for one community's program.

Passengers carried	22,266
Total vehicle miles driven	87,132
Total vehicle hours operated	8,296
Total operating cost	$122,304
Total income from passengers	37,218
Loss funded by taxes	$ 85,086

Using these figures, compute the following:

a. Cost per vehicle mile _____

b. Cost per vehicle hour _____

c. Cost per passenger carried _____

d. Average fare _____

e. Cost per mile funded by taxes _____

7. If you were arguing in support of a dial-a-ride program for your community, which of the above figures would you cite? In what context? What other figures might you want to have for the sake of comparison?

_____

_____

_____

CHAPTER 24 Choosing Other Forms of Transportation

APPLICATION ACTIVITY 2

Assume that you live on one coast (east or west) and wish to vacation in a major city on the other. You have been saving for the last three years and have a total of $900 for the trip. You can stay a maximum of ten days. Your transportation, meals, lodging, and entertainment choices are those listed below. Decide when you want to travel and which vacation options you would like to include in your trip. Indicate your answers on the following page along with the reasons for your choices. Note: In any given category, you may select more than one choice as long as there are sufficient funds in your budget.

1. **Transportation**
   a. Airline: charter; night flight, Tues.-Thurs.; $300 round-trip; no meals; ticket purchase 30 days in advance; minimum stay 8 days.
   b. Airline: coach; day flight, Fri.-Mon., $456 round-trip; in-flight meal plus snack, movie; no minimum stay.
   c. Bus: 12 hours one-way; $200 round-trip.
   d. Car: 5 days with stopovers (600 miles per day); unleaded gasoline $.95-$1.15 per gallon along main interstate highways.
   e. Train: private sleeping compartment; 4 days, 3 nights cross-country; $600 round-trip; reserve 3 months in advance.

2. **Lodging**
   a. Hastings Hotel: downtown hotel, older, but well maintained; near theaters, museums, and shopping district; restaurant and coffee shop; $55-$75 per night, double.
   b. The Lighthouse: 65 miles from center city, oceanfront location; 19th-century lighthouse and adjacent buildings converted into a European-style bed-and-breakfast inn; rooms small, furnishings minimal; no TV; maximum stay 3 days, $25 per night, double; discounts for students and seniors.
   c. The Park Lloyd: newly built 37-story hotel in the downtown financial district; rooms small but well designed with air-conditioning and cable TV; 4 theme restaurants, live entertainment nightly; 40 shops and boutiques opening onto 10-story garden court; $95-$135 per night, double.
   d. Treadway Motel: 15 miles from center city; part of an international motel chain, large rooms, air-conditioned with color TV, swimming pool, restaurant, and coffee shop; $35-$45 per night, double.
   e. Vicarage Gate Inn: old town historic area; mansion converted into a luxury inn; all rooms distinctively appointed with antiques; impeccable service includes newspaper, fresh-cut flowers, and tea served daily in one's room; $250-$600 per night, double; reservation required 3-6 months in advance.

3. **Meals**
   a. Choi's: 16-page menu, over 200 distinctive Chinese dishes; Fri. and Sat. evenings, special 12-course dinner ($20 per person, minimum party of six); open 11:30 a.m. to 10:30 p.m. Tues.-Sun., closed Mon.
   b. Donald's Family Restaurants: "Quality food at reasonable prices in all 50 states and the District of Columbia"; breakfasts from $1.99, lunches and dinners from $3.25; always open.
   c. La Grande Vitesse: French cafeteria; "Quality Food at Quality Prices"; specials daily (entree, 1 vegetable, roll; beverage extra) $4.50-$7.25; open daily, lunch and dinner only.
   d. McJacknBurger: cheeseburgers and fries for breakfast, lunch, and dinner; $2.13 without beverage; open daily, 6:30 a.m. to 10:30 p.m.
   e. Nature's Best: emphasis on salt-free, sugar-free, fat-free cooking; fish and chicken dishes a specialty; fixed price meal daily (salad, hearty soup or entree, bread/roll, fresh fruit, beverage) $5.50; no red meat, coffee/tea, or carbonated beverages served; open noon to 10 p.m., Mon.-Fri.

4. **Entertainment**
   a. Baseball/football game: collegiate; tickets $4.50-$8.50.
   b. Movie: first run; admission $6 per person per show, no discounts or passes (bargain matinees, Mon.-Thurs., $3.50).
   c. Guided tour: morning major landmarks and historic sites, including walking tour of old town and city hall; 2-hour lunch break at city art museum; afternoon financial district, port, Chinatown, and 2-hour walking tour of the city zoo; $18 excluding cafeteria lunch.
   d. Theater: revival of "My Fair Lady"; evenings $35-$45, matinees (Sat. and Sun. only) $30-$40.
   e. Thrills and Chills Theme Park*: "The scariest rides in the East/West"; located 24 miles from center city; admissions— Faint of Heart (6 rides) $15; Nerves of Steel (9 rides) $17.50; Probably a Stuntman (12 rides) $20. *Closed Wed.

Destination: _____ coast to _____ coast

Dates selected: _____ Why? _____

_____

1. Transportation: _____
   Why? _____
   _____
   _____
   _____
   _____

2. Lodging: _____
   Why? _____
   _____
   _____
   _____
   _____

3. Meals: _____
   Why? _____
   _____
   _____
   _____
   _____

4. Entertainment: _____
   Why? _____
   _____
   _____
   _____
   _____

UNIT 7 LAB Transportation and Travel

BUYING A CAR FOR ALL REASONS

Unit 7 provides you with the basic guidelines for buying and owning a car and for planning a motoring vacation. In this lab, you will follow those guidelines as you plan the purchase of a car to be used both for commuting and for taking a twoweek driving trip to visit colleges.

TOOLS

1. *Consumer Reports* and other consumer magazines
2. Car and driving magazines
3. Newspaper, magazine, TV, and radio advertisements for cars
4. A travel atlas
5. Travel guidebooks
6. College guidebooks

PROCEDURES

Read the lab in your textbook and complete each activity using the space provided below.

Step A

Car #1: _____

_____

Car #2: _____

_____

_____

Car #3: _____

_____

_____

Step B

Car Prices and Payment Plans

Make and model	Price		Monthly payment	
	Standard options	All desired options	Standard options	All desired options

Step C

Service costs for car #1: _____

_____

Service costs for car #2: _____

Service costs for car #3: _____

Step D
College/university #1: _____

College/university #2: _____

College/university #3: _____

Step E
Obtain the maps you need and use highlighter to show your planned routes.

LAB REPORT
Step F
Use your car chart and your notes to answer the following questions.

1. For each car you considered, what was the price difference between a model with only standard equipment and one with all the options you wanted?

   _____

2. Which option was the most expensive?

   _____

3. What was the average finance charge for the models you considered?

   _____

4. What was the average cost of routine maintenance at 7,500 miles (or at the first recommended maintenance period) for each model?

   _____

5. What were the total college-trip costs for fuel and lodging if you and your relative stayed in budget accommodations? if you both stayed in more luxurious lodgings?

   _____

Step G
Using a word processor or a typewriter, write a two-page report explaining which car you would select and how price, performance, reliability, and intended use affected your decision.

UNIT 8 Buying Clothing

ATTITUDE INVENTORY

Before you begin Unit 8, take stock of your attitudes by completing the following inventory. Read each statement and decide how you feel about it—agree, disagree, or undecided. Write your answers in the blanks.

1. When purchasing clothing, always choose the best quality available.

2. A generous cut and solid construction are indications of good garment quality.

3. Blending manufactured and natural fibers results in a weaker fabric.

4. Labels telling how to care for clothing are of little value.

5. Purchases of the clothing you want should be based on a thorough knowledge of the clothing you already have.

6. "Making do" with what we have is a good policy in some budget categories but a very poor policy where clothing is concerned.

7. Classic styles are dull and should be avoided as wardrobe additions.

8. The price tag on a given clothing item is not the best indicator of quality.

9. Information on a tag such as "Compare at $30" is helpful information to the consumer.

10. "Never throw clothing out—it's bound to come back in style" is good advice.

11. Clothing "styles" are only as good as they look on you.

12. A good rule of thumb for choosing synthetic fabrics and blends is to determine if they look and feel more natural than synthetic.

13. Fashion trends are popular for only a short period of time and therefore should be ignored.

14. A good shopper considers several different places to buy clothing.

15. Shopping in discount stores is a mistake—you get what you pay for.

1. _____

2. _____

3. _____

4. _____

5. _____

6. _____

7. _____

8. _____

9. _____

10. _____

11. _____

12. _____

13. _____

14. _____

15. _____

RECHECKING YOUR ATTITUDE

Before going on to the next unit, answer the Attitude Inventory questions a second time. Then compare the two sets of responses. On how many statements have your attitudes changed? Can you account for these shifts in your opinions? What do you know now that you did not know then?

1. When purchasing clothing, always choose the best quality available. 1. _____

2. A generous cut and solid construction are indications of good garment quality. 2. _____

3. Blending manufactured and natural fibers results in a weaker fabric. 3. _____

4. Labels telling how to care for clothing are of little value. 4. _____

5. Purchases of the clothing you want should be based on a thorough knowledge of the clothing you already have. 5. _____

6. "Making do" with what we have is a good policy in some budget categories but a very poor policy where clothing is concerned. 6. _____

7. Classic styles are dull and should be avoided as wardrobe additions. 7. _____

8. The price tag on a given clothing item is not the best indicator of quality. 8. _____

9. Information on a tag such as "Compare at $30" is helpful information to the consumer. 9. _____

10. "Never throw clothing out—it's bound to come back in style" is good advice. 10. _____

11. Clothing "styles" are only as good as they look on you. 11. _____

12. A good rule of thumb for choosing synthetic fabrics and blends is to determine if they look and feel more natural than synthetic. 12. _____

13. Fashion trends are popular for only a short period of time and therefore should be ignored. 13. _____

14. A good shopper considers several different places to buy clothing. 14. _____

15. Shopping in discount stores is a mistake—you get what you pay for. 15. _____

Answers changed _____ Why? _____

_____

_____

_____

_____

_____

_____

_____

_____

_____

_____

_____

_____

CHAPTER 25 *Planning a Wardrobe*

REVIEWING CONSUMER TERMS

Build a crossword puzzle using the terms below. Use the space below to arrange your entries. Then write short definitions for them.

accessories   inventory

coordinated   mix-and-match

garment   wardrobe

CHAPTER **25** *Planning a Wardrobe*

REVIEWING FACTS AND IDEAS

1. What features should you look for when planning your wardrobe?

   _____

   _____

   _____

   _____

2. How can you develop a suitable wardrobe?

   _____

   _____

   _____

   _____

3. If you do an inventory of your clothes and accessories and find items that you don't want anymore, what are the options available to you?

   _____

   _____

   _____

   _____

4. How can you make your wardrobe last longer?

   _____

   _____

   _____

   _____

5. How can advance planning help you to be happier with what you buy?

   _____

   _____

   _____

   _____

   _____

CHAPTER 25 *Planning a Wardrobe*

APPLICATION ACTIVITY 1

Assume that you are asked to help a younger brother or sister do a wardrobe inventory. What solutions would you recommend for each of the problems listed below?

1. Raincoat (no longer repels water):

_____

_____

2. Shoes (heels run down, hole in one sole; uppers good):

_____

_____

3. Jeans (bottoms frayed; fabric weakened and wearing through at the seams):

_____

_____

4. Winter coat (too small across the shoulders, too short).

_____

_____

5. Sweatshirt (poor color; sleeves and length too long):

_____

_____

6. Jacket (pocket ripped beyond mending; elbows worn through):

_____

_____

7. Sweater (faded and stretched, but otherwise usable):

_____

_____

_____

8. Two tops, two pairs of shorts (all in good condition; from different sets, however, and poorly coordinated):

_____

_____

_____

9. Jogging suit/sweats (one year old, never worn; one size too large):

_____

_____

_____

CHAPTER 25 *Planning a Wardrobe*

APPLICATION ACTIVITY 2

If you are like most people, your present wardrobe is not very well coordinated. Mix-and-match possibilities are limited because of poor color and style choices. To correct this situation, you will have to plan future purchases carefully.

1. Begin by doing a wardrobe inventory on the chart below. If you need more space, duplicate the column headings on a sheet of ruled paper and continue your listing there. *Note:* Inventory clothing for the current season only—fall/winter or spring/summer.

Wardrobe Item	Color	Style	Action Needed			New Purchases	
			Donate/ Discard/ Exchange	Repair Recycle	Dry Clean/ Launder	Items to Buy	Est. Cost

2. Study the list of clothing you have on hand. Using it, select one basic and two coordinating colors. (For example, navy blue plus green and white because you have a navy blue suit with a green, white, and navy plaid blouse/shirt.) Circle all the items in your wardrobe that already fall within this palette. Then on the planning chart below, list the items you will need to acquire over the next few years to round out this wardrobe and maximize its mix-and-match possibilities.

Items to Buy	Style	Basic Color: _____	Coord. Color #1:_____	Coord. Color #2:_____

CHAPTER **26** *Shopping for Clothes*

REVIEWING CONSUMER TERMS

Use each of the following terms in a sentence to demonstrate you know its meaning.

blends	natural fibers
classics	off-price outlet
factory outlets	permanent care label
fads	Sanforized
hangtags	synthetic fibers

_____

_____

_____

_____

_____

_____

_____

_____

_____

_____

_____

_____

_____

_____

_____

_____

_____

_____

_____

_____

_____

_____

_____

_____

_____

_____

_____

_____

_____

_____

CHAPTER 26 *Shopping for Clothes*

REVIEWING FACTS AND IDEAS

1. What five factors should you keep in mind when shopping for clothes?

   _____

   _____

   _____

   _____

2. List the advantages and disadvantages of natural and synthetic fibers.

   Advantages (natural): _____

   _____

   _____

   _____

   Advantages (synthetic): _____

   _____

   _____

   _____

3. What should you look for in examining clothing for quality workmanship?

   _____

   _____

   _____

   _____

   _____

   _____

4. How are permanent-care labels of value to the consumer?

   _____

   _____

   _____

   _____

5. List common shopping problems.

   _____

   _____

   _____

   _____

   _____

CHAPTER 26 *Shopping for Clothes*

APPLICATION ACTIVITY 1

Study the permanent care labels shown below. Then answer the questions that follow.

Garment 1

```
60% RAYON
20% POLY.
10% SILK
6% WOOL
4% FLAX
DRY CLEAN ONLY
```

Garment 2

```
70% COTTON          30% RAYON
Hand wash in cool water with mild detergent.
Rinse thoroughly keeping water clear of
excess dye. Do not use any cold water wool
washes. Dry flat. No bleach. Cool iron.
```

Garment 3

```
100% Cotton
Hand Wash Cold.
Do Not Twist.
Reshape. Dry Flat.
Do Not Dry Clean.
```

Garment 4

```
100% POLYESTER
MACHINE WASH WARM DELICATE
TUMBLE DRY LOW
REMOVE PROMPTLY
COOL IRON
```

1. a. Which garment(s) are made from blends? 1. a. _____

   b. Which garment(s) are made from natural fibers exclusively? b. _____

2. a. Which garment(s) can be machine washed? 2. a. _____

   b. Which garment(s) must be hand washed? b. _____

   c. Which garment(s) cannot be washed at all? c. _____

   d. Which garment(s) can be washed in hot water? d. _____

3. Which garment(s) must be ironed using minimal heat? 3. _____

4. What does the instruction "Dry flat" (as in labels 2 and 3) mean? Why do you think it is included?

   _____

   _____

   _____

5. Look at the label for garment 1. What is "poly"? What is flax?

   _____

   _____

   _____

6. Which garment(s) might fade or "run" when washed? How do you know?

   _____

   _____

   _____

CHAPTER **26** *Shopping for Clothes*

APPLICATION ACTIVITY 2

Before buying clothes, you need to evaluate the quality, fit, and overall appearance of the garments you want to buy. Use the following checklist to evaluate at least three garments you are considering. Then answer the question at the bottom of the page.

	Excellent	Good	Fair	Poor

CONSTRUCTION

1. Seams (generous allowance, flat, secure)

2. Stitching (small, evenly spaced)

3. Reinforcements at points of stress

4. Design that matches

5. Fasteners/buttons/buttonholes (secure, neatly made)

6. Hems (deep enough, stitches not visible from front)

7. Collars/lapels (points flat and smooth)

FIT

1. Full cut, not skimpy

2. Overall comfort

3. Special fit (at waist, hip area, chest, sleeves, length, shoulders, neckline)

STYLE

1. Suitability of fabric (feel, durability, ease of care, special features needed)

2. Suitability of color and design

3. Style that fits the image you want

COST TO WEAR

1. Cost _____

2. Plus estimated cleaning costs _____

3. Divided by estimated times to wear _____

4. Equals cost to wear _____

QUESTION

Did using this survey help you make a better purchasing decision? Did any results surprise you? Why or why not?

_____

_____

_____

UNIT 8 LAB Buying Clothing

PLANNING A WARDROBE FOR A NEW LIFE

Unit 8 presents the practical steps needed to inventory your wardrobe and to make wise clothing purchases. This lab will help you practice what you've learned as you plan a wardrobe for college and a part-time office job.

TOOLS

1. Almanacs (*Places Rated Almanac,* by David Savageau and Richard Boyer, Prentice-Hall, 1993, is particularly helpful for researching weather conditions in specific locations.)
2. Travel and college guidebooks
3. Newspapers
4. Fashion magazines
5. Direct-mail advertisements

PROCEDURES

Read the lab in your textbook and then complete each activity used the space provided below.

Step A

Climate northeastern United States

Summer: _____

Winter: _____

Climate southwestern United States

Summer: _____

Winter: _____

Step B

Northeastern Climate	Southwestern Climate
_____	_____
_____	_____
_____	_____
_____	_____
_____	_____
_____	_____
_____	_____
_____	_____

Step C

Discount store: _____

_____

Specialty/department store: _____

_____

Outlet store: _____

_____

Lab Report
Step D

Use your wardrobe inventory, budgets, and shopping lists to answer the following questions.

1. If you had purchased every item on your list, what would your total cost have been at each store for the Northeastern clothing and the Southwestern clothing?

   _____

   _____

   _____

   _____

2. What was the average price of the items?

   _____

   _____

3. Select one item that was sold at both stores. What was the difference in price? Speculate on why there might be a price difference.

   _____

   _____

   _____

   _____

4. Review your shopping notes. Make two final northeastern and southwestern clothing lists. For these lists, write the items you could actually purchase with your budget, where you would purchase each item, and the prices.

   _____

   _____

   _____

   _____

Step E

Using a word processor or typewriter, write a two-page report that explains your new wardrobe choices in terms of need, price, quality, and utility.

UNIT 9 Buying Food, Medicines, and Cosmetics

ATTITUDE INVENTORY

Before you begin Unit 9, take stock of your attitudes by completing the following inventory. Read each statement and decide how you feel about it—agree, disagree, or undecided. Write your answers in the blanks.

1. The majority of Americans are well nourished.

2. Shopping for groceries once a week is an old-fashioned idea and a poor practice to follow given the convenience of modern supermarkets.

3. A perishable food should be discarded once the date on its package is reached.

4. Fiber has no nutritional value.

5. You must be unemployed to receive food stamps.

6. Food products must carry a list of all ingredients in order of weight somewhere on their labels.

7. Name brand foods offer consumers better quality than store brand foods.

8. To be sold over the counter, a drug must have no side effects.

9. Convenience foods are designed to save consumers time and money.

10. No skin-care product can prevent sunburn.

11. The average American diet contains too much fat and sugar and not enough complex carbohydrates.

12. Drugs must be tested to the satisfaction of the FDA before they can be marketed in the U.S.

13. How much fat a piece of red meat contains will determine how tender it is.

14. All ingredients in a cosmetic must be listed on the label.

15. Vitamins and minerals are needed in small, but correct, amounts for good health.

1. _____

2. _____

3. _____

4. _____

5. _____

6. _____

7. _____

8. _____

9. _____

10. _____

11. _____

12. _____

13. _____

14. _____

15. _____

RECHECKING YOUR ATTITUDE

Before going on to the next unit, answer the Attitude Inventory questions a second time. Then compare the two sets of responses. On how many statements have your attitudes changed? Can you account for these shifts in your opinions? What do you know now that you did not know then?

1. The majority of Americans are well nourished.   1. _____

2. Shopping for groceries once a week is an old-fashioned idea and a poor practice to follow given the convenience of modern supermarkets.   2. _____

3. A perishable food should be discarded once the date on its package is reached.   3. _____

4. Fiber has no nutritional value.   4. _____

5. You must be unemployed to receive food stamps.   5. _____

6. Food products must carry a list of all ingredients in order of weight somewhere on their labels.   6. _____

7. Name brand foods offer consumers better quality than store brand foods.   7. _____

8. To be sold over the counter, a drug must have no side effects.   8. _____

9. Convenience foods are designed to save consumers time and money.   9. _____

10. No skin-care product can prevent sunburn.   10. _____

11. The average American diet contains too much fat and sugar and not enough complex carbohydrates.   11. _____

12. Drugs must be tested to the satisfaction of the FDA before they can be marketed in the U.S.   12. _____

13. How much fat a piece of red meat contains will determine how tender it is.   13. _____

14. All ingredients in a cosmetic must be listed on the label.   14. _____

15. Vitamins and minerals are needed in small, but correct, amounts for good health.   15. _____

Answers changed _____ Why? _____

_____

_____

_____

_____

_____

_____

_____

_____

_____

_____

_____

_____

CHAPTER 27 Fundamentals of Good Nutrition

REVIEWING CONSUMER TERMS

Use each of the following terms in a paragraph to demonstrate you know its meaning.

anabolic steroids

anorexia nervosa

bulimia nervosa

calories

cholesterol

complex carbohydrates

empty-calorie food

fiber

malnourished

nutrients

obesity

recommended daily allowances (RDA)

_____

_____

_____

_____

_____

_____

_____

_____

_____

_____

_____

_____

_____

_____

_____

_____

_____

_____

_____

_____

_____

_____

_____

_____

CHAPTER 27 *Fundamentals of Good Nutrition*

REVIEWING FACTS AND IDEAS

1. Experts recommend that you eat dark green or deep yellow vegetables several times a day. Using the information in Figure 27-1, page 429 in your text, for support, explain why.

_____

_____

_____

_____

2. Identify common nutrient deficiencies found in teens and suggest ways to prevent them.

_____

_____

_____

_____

3. Identify the five basic food groups and indicate how many servings from each group are recommended per day.

_____

_____

_____

_____

4. Explain why the food groups are placed as they are on the Food Pyramid.

_____

_____

_____

_____

5. What are the six dietary guidelines?

_____

_____

_____

_____

6. What are some eating and exercise disorders and reasons for these problem behaviors?

_____

_____

_____

_____

CHAPTER 27 *Fundamentals of Good Nutrition*

APPLICATION ACTIVITY 1

Use what you have learned about good nutrition to evaluate the eating habits of the two people described below.

Beakfast	Lunch	Dinner
Hard roll and low-sugar spread Tea with lemon	Pineapple chunks (1/2 c.) Low-fat cottage cheese (1/2 c.) Diet soda	Peas, carrots, stewed tomatoes (1/2 c. each) Baked potato (1/2 c. plain) Crackers Tea with lemon

A. Marcia is sixteen and extremely figure conscious. "I eat for my jeans," she explains with a laugh and a groan. "You would too if you knew what they cost me." Possibly her jeans are costing Marcia more than she realizes. Study her meals for one day, then answer the questions that follow.

1. How well do Marcia's meals meet the requirements of the five food groups in the food pyramid? Note any omissions. Do the foods chosen follow the recommended number of servings for the day?

_____

_____

_____

_____

_____

2. How well do Marcia's meals meet the six U.S. Dietary guidelines described in your textbook?

_____

_____

_____

_____

_____

3. How can Marcia both improve her diet and save her jeans?

_____

_____

_____

_____

_____

_____

B. Jeff is twenty-seven and an accountant. He is also overweight. "I can't figure it out," he complains. "I exercise twice a week, eat right, have all the things you're supposed to—meat, vegetables, milk. I even snack healthy—nothing but fruit between meals. And still I'm overweight. How come? Tell me, how come?" Study Jeff's three typical meals and see if you can help him.

Breakfast	Lunch	Dinner
Oatmeal with butter and syrup Ham and three-egg omelette Blueberry muffin Milk (Midmorning snack: canned peaches)	Double cheeseburger (with pickle and ketchup) French fries (large order) Vanilla shake	Fried chicken (half) Mashed potatoes Corn (1 ear) Dinner rolls (2) (Evening snack: banana and milk)

1. How well do Jeff's meals meet the requirements of the basic food groups? Note any omissions.

_____

_____

_____

_____

_____

_____

2. How well do Jeff's meals meet the recommendations for essential reductions in and additions to the average American diet?

_____

_____

_____

_____

_____

_____

3. How can Jeff maintain a healthful diet and still lose weight?

_____

_____

_____

_____

_____

_____

_____

CHAPTER **27** *Fundamentals of Good Nutrition*

APPLICATION ACTIVITY 2

Use your knowledge about recommended foods to plan your own meals that will meet dietary guidelines.

1. Using the space beside the food pyramid, write the names of your favorite foods for each of the five basic food groups. Label each food group on the pyramid.

2. Review the nutrition charts in your textbook chapter. Identify the foods listed that you do not eat regularly. What nutrients/functions do they provide? Indicate the food group for each food.

Foods I should try to eat more regularly:	Nutrients/Functions	Food Group

3. Develop a menu plan for two days using the recommended number of servings in each of the five food groups. Include the foods you listed in questions 1 and 2. Make sure your choices follow the U.S. Dietary Guidelines.

Day 1		
Breakfast	Lunch	Dinner

Day 2		
Breakfast	Lunch	Dinner

4. How well did you do? What foods do you plan to eat more of, and less of, as a result of your food planning?

_____

_____

_____

_____

_____

_____

_____

_____

_____

Chapter 28 *Smart Shopping Techniques*

REVIEWING CONSUMER TERMS

Use each of the following terms in a paragraph to demonstrate you know its meaning.

convenience foods   nutrient density
expiration date   open date
impulse buying   pull date
name brand   store brand
net weight   unit price

_____

_____

_____

_____

_____

_____

_____

_____

_____

_____

_____

_____

_____

_____

_____

_____

_____

_____

_____

_____

_____

_____

_____

_____

_____

_____

Chapter 28 Smart Shopping Techniques

REVIEWING FACTS AND IDEAS

1. Why is the order in which ingredients are listed on food labels important?

_____

_____

2. Why is planning for your shopping trip important?

_____

_____

_____

3. How are name brands, store brands, and generic products likely to compare in cost and quality?

_____

_____

_____

_____

4. Where would you find the unit price of a product and how would you use that information?

_____

_____

_____

_____

5. How would you select each of the following?

   a. A tender steak _____

   b. The freshest eggs _____

   c. The best oranges _____

   d. The freshest carrots _____

6. What are some reasons for high food prices?

_____

_____

_____

_____

7. How do stores encourage impulse purchases?

_____

_____

_____

_____

Chapter 28   *Smart Shopping Techniques*

APPLICATION ACTIVITY 1

Unit pricing and product labeling can help shoppers choose between items that would otherwise be very difficult to compare. Consider these situations.

You want to buy a container of juice. Here are your choices.

Brand	Size (oz.)	Price ($)	Unit Price (¢ per oz.)
Name	15.25	.75	4.9
Local	15.25	.65	4.3
Store	15	.59	3.9
Generic	15	.99	6.6

1. Cover the unit price column and try to decide which brand is the best buy. What difficulties do you face when you do not know the price?

   _____

   _____

   _____

2. Now uncover the unit price column and try to decide. Place a check (✔) beside the brand you would buy. Is this the result you would have expected? Why or why not?

   _____

   _____

3. You need approximately two cups of corn for a recipe. In terms of taste and preparation, it makes no difference to you whether the product is canned or frozen. Your options are given below. Complete the charts by computing the unit prices. Then check (✔) the item you would buy.

	Brand	Size (oz.)	Price ($)	Unit Price (¢ per oz.)
Canned	Name	15.25	.65	
	Local	15.25	.65	
	Store	15.25	.50	
	Gourmet	11	.79	

	Brand	Size (oz.)	Price ($)	Unit Price (¢ per oz.)
Frozen	Name	10	1.45	
	Local	16	1.15	
	Store	16	.69	
	Gourmet	16	1.49	

4. In terms of cost, is there any difference between canned and frozen corn? What factors do you think account for this result?

   _____

   _____

Chapter 28 Smart Shopping Techniques

APPLICATION ACTIVITY 2

Shown below is a nutrition label from a box of a cereal product. Study the label, then use the information in it and your textbook chapter to answer the questions that follow.

1. What product do you think is described by the label? How can you tell?

   _____

   _____

   _____

2. According to the label, how many servings does the box contain?

   _____

3. Will you get exactly the same number of servings? Why?

   _____

   _____

   _____

4. What effect does a difference in serving size have on the nutritional information on the label?

   _____

   _____

   _____

   _____

5. What are some of this product's advantages?

   _____

   _____

   _____

6. How could you boost the vitamin and mineral content of this product?

   _____

   _____

   _____

NUTRITION FACTS Serving size 1/2 cup dry (40g) Servings Per Container 30 Amount per Serving		
	Cereal Alone	with 1/2 cup Vit. A & D fortified skim milk
Calories	150	190
Calories from Fat	25	25
	% Daily Value*	
Total Fat 3g*	5%	5%
Saturated Fat 0.5g	2%	2%
Polyunsaturated Fat 1g		
Monounsaturated Fat 1g		
Cholesterol 0mg	0%	0%
Sodium 0mg	0%	3%
Total Carbohydrate 27g	9%	11%
Dietary Fiber 4g	15%	15%
Soluble Fiber 2g		
Insoluble Fiber 2g		
Sugars 1g		
Protein 5g		
Vitamin A	0%	4%
Vitamin C	0%	2%
Calcium	0%	15%
Iron	10%	10%

*Percent Daily Values are based on a 2,000 calorie diet. Your daily values may be higher or lower depending on your calorie needs:

		2,000	2,500
Calories		2,000	2,500
Total Fat	Less than	65 g	60 g
Sat Fat	Less than	20 g	25 g
Cholesterol	Less than	300 mg	300 mg
Sodium	Less than	2,400 mg	2,400 mg
Total carbohydrate		300g	375g
Dietary Fiber		25g	30g

Calories per gram - Fat 9 • Carbohydrates 4 • Protein 4
Ingredients: 100% natural rolled oats.

7. Which items on the label are better if they have a lower Daily Value percentage? a higher Daily Value percentage?

   _____

   _____

CHAPTER 29 Drugs and Cosmetics

REVIEWING CONSUMER TERMS

Use each of the following terms in a sentence to demonstrate you know its meaning.

cosmetics
drugs
over-the-counter (OTC) drugs
prescription drugs

registered pharmacist
side effects
tampering

_____

_____

_____

_____

_____

_____

_____

_____

_____

_____

_____

_____

_____

_____

_____

_____

_____

_____

_____

_____

_____

_____

_____

_____

_____

_____

_____

CHAPTER 29   *Drugs and Cosmetics*

REVIEWING FACTS AND IDEAS

1. Why is the distinction between drugs and cosmetics important to consumers?

2. Identify two basic types of medicines.

3. What questions should you ask your doctor when he or she gives you a prescription?

4. Summarize the risks involved with taking over-the-counter drugs.

5. Why is ingredient labeling on cosmetics not as helpful to consumers as ingredient labeling on foods?

6. What devices can be used to prevent product tampering?

7. Describe how to properly select skin and hair care products.

8. Identify characteristics of skin protection products.

CHAPTER 29 Drugs and Cosmetics

APPLICATION ACTIVITY 1

Visit a local supermarket or pharmacy. Select an over-the-counter drug—a cough medicine, headache remedy, or digestive aid, for example. Read the fine print on the package and use the information to answer the following questions.

1. What is the name of the product?

_____

2. What is the name and address of the manufacturer, distributor, or packer?

_____

3. How much does a full package contain?

_____

4. For what purpose is the product used?

_____

5. What are the directions for the product's safe use?

_____

6. Are there any special warnings or cautions? How are these indicated?

_____

7. Are there any side effects? If so, identify them.

_____

8. What are the active ingredients in the product?

_____

9. Note any unfamiliar technical or medical terms that appear on the product's package. List these below. Then look up the words in an unabridged or medical dictionary and write out brief definitions.

_____

10. a. Briefly scan the packages of three other OTC drugs (preferably of an entirely different type). Then fill out the chart below by checking the items that are present.

OTC DRUGS—PACKAGE INFORMATION

Product Name	Mfr.	Contents	Use	Direc.	Caut.	Side Effects	Ingred.

b. Do the packages contain similar or different information? How do you account for this result?

_____

11. OTC drugs must be sold in tamper-resistant packages. What antitampering devices did you observe in your product survey?

_____

CHAPTER 29 Drugs and Cosmetics

APPLICATION ACTIVITY 2

Read the following paragraphs, then use the information to answer the questions below.

Have you noticed magazine ads for sunlamps and tanning beds? The models in the ads look great—tanned, smiling, young, and healthy. Having a great tan may sound appealing now, but research shows that skin damage can occur from the use of such products.

Sunlamps and tanning beds give off UV radiation—both UVA and UVB. The radiation causes you to tan, but it's also harmful to skin cells. Even getting just a little bit of tan may not be safe. By using such products, you are adding to the radiation you already get from the sun. Over a lifetime, you can accumulate too much radiation. The result is an increased risk of skin cancer, premature skin aging, reduced immunity to diseases, skin and eye burns, cataracts, and blood vessel damage. Getting too much radiation while you are taking medications may also make your skin more sensitive and more prone to damage.

The next time you think about tanning, ask yourself whether you're willing to take the risks.

1. Why isn't a "safe" tan possible?

   _____

   _____

2. What are some risks, other than cancer, from UV radiation?

   _____

   _____

3. What do you think is wrong with the following advertising claim? "Our modern facility uses advanced European UVA technology to provide you a safe, convenient, and beautiful tan."

   _____

   _____

4. What problems are each of the following FDA requirements designed to avoid? How effective do you think each requirement is in preventing problems?

   a. Tanning salons must provide eye protection for customers.

   _____

   _____

   _____

   b. Tanning salons must use timers to limit customer exposure to UV lamps.

   _____

   _____

   _____

5. Who should never use tanning devices?

   _____

   _____

   _____

UNIT 9 LAB Buying Food, Medicines, and Cosmetics

PLANNING A HEALTHY DIET

Unit 9 presents the basics of a well-balanced diet and discusses techniques for smart food, drug, and cosmetics shopping. In this lab, you will apply those techniques to planning a shopping trip to buy a week's worth of food and other necessities for your family.

TOOLS

1. Lists of the basic food groups and common nutrients
2. Healthful recipes
3. Food sections from local newspapers
4. A guide to the calorie and fat gram counts of particular foods

PROCEDURES

Read the lab in your textbook and complete each activity using the space provided below.

Step A

Family Members

Name		Age	
_____		_____	
_____		_____	
_____		_____	
_____		_____	
_____		_____	

Calorie/food reference books: _____

_____

_____

Step B

Food	Nutrients Provided	Food	Nutrients Provided
_____	_____	_____	_____
_____	_____	_____	_____
_____	_____	_____	_____
_____	_____	_____	_____
_____	_____	_____	_____
_____	_____	_____	_____
_____	_____	_____	_____

Step C

Use separate paper to list the foods you need for the week's meals, the OTC drug, and a cosmetic item.

Step D

Store #1: _____

Store #2: _____

LAB REPORT
Step E

Use your week of menus, your shopping list, and your price-comparison charts to answer the questions below.

1. What was your total grocery bill at each store if

   a. you bought only national brands? _____

   b. you bought store brands when available? _____

   c. you bought generic brands when available? _____

2. Using your totals from 1a, 1b, and 1c above, determine the average expenditure at both stores for each day's meals.

   _____

   _____

3. Which menus were less expensive to make and what caused them to be less expensive?

   _____

   _____

   _____

4. How did the quality of produce, meat, and fish at the "low-price" store differ from the quality of those items at the "high-quality" store?

   _____

   _____

5. If there was a price difference between the stores on over-the-counter drugs and cosmetics, what would cause such a difference?

   _____

   _____

Step E

Using a word processor or a typewriter, write a two-page report that explains the cost and the health benefits of a healthful diet and that discusses the differences between the two stores on the basis of the cost and apparent quality of the items.

UNIT 10 Selecting Housing

ATTITUDE INVENTORY

Before you begin Unit 10, take stock of your attitudes by completing the following inventory. Read each statement and decide how you feel about it—agree, disagree, or undecided. Write your answers in the blanks.

1. A consumer needs to have a general knowledge of what is in his or her lease, but a line-for-line reading is unnecessary.

2. The best source of information about operating an appliance is the service department of the store selling it.

3. A moving company can pack and unpack your belongings as well as transport them.

4. Mobile homes can be hitched to the family car and towed from place to place.

5. For average consumers, the best way to buy a home is to have it custom-built.

6. A person who rents an apartment has the right to privacy.

7. Those who spend 35 percent of their income for rent are spending a reasonable amount for that purpose.

8. Wise consumers wait until they can pay cash before buying a home.

9. Owning a home is an important part of "the good life."

10. Over the years, houses have proved to be very poor investments.

11. A couple earning $40,000 a year probably cannot afford a house costing more than $100,000.

12. It is possible to buy an apartment.

13. There is only one standard for judging a piece of upholstered furniture—is it comfortable?

14. Poor workmanship in home construction is a common consumer problem.

15. If a defect or failure is not listed in an appliance's warranty, the buyer is not protected against it.

1. _____

2. _____

3. _____

4. _____

5. _____

6. _____

7. _____

8. _____

9. _____

10. _____

11. _____

12. _____

13. _____

14. _____

15. _____

RECHECKING YOUR ATTITUDE

Before going on to the next unit, answer the Attitude Inventory questions a second time. Then compare the two sets of responses. On how many statements have your attitudes changed? Can you account for these shifts in your opinions? What do you know now that you did not know then?

1. A consumer needs to have a general knowledge of what is in his or her lease, but a line-for-line reading is unnecessary.

1. _____

2. The best source of information about operating an appliance is the service department of the store selling it.

2. _____

3. A moving company can pack and unpack your belongings as well as transport them.

3. _____

4. Mobile homes can be hitched to the family car and towed from place to place.

4. _____

5. For average consumers, the best way to buy a home is to have it custom-built.

5. _____

6. A person who rents an apartment has the right to privacy.

6. _____

7. Those who spend 35 percent of their income for rent are spending a reasonable amount for that purpose.

7. _____

8. Wise consumers wait until they can pay cash before buying a home.

8. _____

9. Owning a home is an important part of "the good life."

9. _____

10. Over the years, houses have proved to be very poor investments.

10. _____

11. A couple earning $40,000 a year probably cannot afford a house costing more than $100,000.

11. _____

12. It is possible to buy an apartment.

12. _____

13. There is only one standard for judging a piece of upholstered furniture— is it comfortable?

13. _____

14. Poor workmanship in home construction is a common consumer problem.

14. _____

15. If a defect or failure is not listed in an appliance's warranty, the buyer is not protected against it.

15. _____

Answers changed _____ Why? _____

_____

_____

_____

_____

_____

_____

_____

_____

_____

_____

CHAPTER 30 Renting an Apartment

REVIEWING CONSUMER TERMS

Use the following in a short story entitled "The Day I Decided to Rent an Apartment."

efficiency apartment
evict
landlord
lease

security deposit
sublet
tenant

_____

_____

_____

_____

_____

_____

_____

_____

_____

_____

_____

_____

_____

_____

_____

_____

_____

_____

_____

_____

_____

_____

_____

_____

_____

_____

_____

_____

CHAPTER **30** *Renting an Apartment*

REVIEWING FACTS AND IDEAS

1. Explain three advantages of renting an apartment.

   _____

   _____

   _____

   _____

2. What are four factors to consider when defining your housing needs?

   _____

   _____

   _____

   _____

3. Suggest several sources of information about apartments for rent.

   _____

   _____

   _____

   _____

   _____

4. What are the basic rights and responsibilities of the tenant and landlord?

   _____

   _____

   _____

   _____

   _____

5. Give four suggestions for making a move go smoothly.

   _____

   _____

   _____

   _____

   _____

   _____

CHAPTER **30** *Renting an Apartment*

APPLICATION ACTIVITY 1

When to move, where to move, and whether to move—all are critical decisions. This is especially true for young people. They are often holding down their first jobs, and funds are limited. More is involved than just housing costs, however. Consider the following examples. Be sure to read each problem all the way through before trying to answer any part.

1. John has been employed by Sampson Brothers for two years. Recently he was promoted to a job at the main office in Hamilton, twenty miles from Claridge where he now lives. Before the promotion, John drove two miles to work each day. The distance increased to twenty-two miles each way when he was transferred to Hamilton.

   John lives in an apartment and pays $375 a month in rent. He could rent the same size apartment for the same amount if he moved to Hamilton. If he moved, John would drive three miles to work each day. It costs 43 cents a mile to operate his car.

   a. How much is John now spending per week on transportation?   a. _____

   b. How much would his weekly transportation costs be if he moved?   b. _____

   c. How much would the move save John in weekly transportation costs?   c. _____

2. Priscilla has been working at a computer factory since her graduation from high school last June. She is living in her parents' home. They provide all of her meals, including brownbag lunches. Her commuting costs to and from work total $80 a month.

   Priscilla is considering the following options, all of which she can afford. Any extra costs, however, would mean a reduction in the amount she can deposit in her savings account each payday.

   a. Renting a furnished room near work for $200 a month. (Because there would be no cooking facilities, this arrangement would mean taking all meals out.)
   b. Renting an efficiency apartment in a complex near the factory for $300 a month and doing her own cooking. (Groceries would cost $130 a month, including a small entertainment allowance.)
   c. Sharing a two-bedroom apartment with two other women from the factory. (Each would contribute $175 a month toward the rent and $120 a month for food.)

   Briefly explain which option Priscilla should take and why.

   _____

   _____

   _____

   _____

   _____

   _____

   _____

   _____

   _____

   _____

   _____

3. Theo and Salonga were married several months ago after meeting on the job at C&E Enterprises. They live in suburban Panorama and commute across town to Tolliver, where C&E is located. Because their car is old and inefficient, commuting is expensive. Theo and Salonga feel that they cannot afford a new automobile. Instead, they are considering a move to shorten their commute.

Salonga and Theo currently pay $425 a month for an unfurnished, two-bedroom apartment (utilities excluded). They can manage this amount easily since their combined take-home pay comes to about $600 a week. They have a joint checking account which contains $1,450 and savings of approximately twice that amount.

Some of the housing options Salonga and Theo have appear below. They are drawn from the classified section of the local newspaper. Read each ad. Then decide whether the couple should rule out the described apartment or investigate it further. In the first case, give the reasons why. In the second, list additional information needed.

a.	$75 wk. Immaculate. Furnd rms, some w/hot plates. Converted motel nr C&E Ent.	a. _____
b.	$400 plus utils 2 bdrm, stv/frig. Off-st pkg. Nr I-280 exit.	b. _____
c.	$575. TRINITY LANE Furnished Apts. Newly dec 2 bdrm, 1 ba. Laun, pkg. charmg garden. Lease & dpst reqd. No pets. Limit 1 child.	c. _____
d.	$400.1 bdrm apt, upstrs pvt home. All utils pd. Beau furnd. Share entr, laun. No pets, children, late hrs, smokg. Apply only if employd & mature. Refs reqd.	d. _____
e.	$450 up. Singls, 1 & 2 bdrm apts. Sec complex, elev bldgs, subtrn pkg. Full kitchens, cpt/drps. Pool, gym, clubhse. Small pet OK w/ dpst. Xlnt locat nr bus & shopg.	e. _____
f.	$625 plus utils. FAMILIES WELCOME! 3 bdrm, 2 ba. Cpts/drps, laun. Pool, playgrd, pkg bldg.	f. _____
g.	$785. Triplex penthse. Classic 2 bdrm & den, 2M2 ba. Firepl, beam ceilgs, carport, balc. Quiet hillside locat, view.	g. _____
	PANORAMA	
h.	$325. 2 rms, ba. Furnd. Utils pd.	h. _____

CHAPTER 30 Renting an Apartment

APPLICATION ACTIVITY 2

Study the lease that appears below. Note especially the restrictions on and duties of the tenant. Then answer the questions on the following page.

RENTAL AGREEMENT
(MONTH - TO - MONTH TENANCY)

THIS AGREEMENT, entered into this ___1st___ day of ___October___, 19__96__, by and between

___TOTAL CONTROL MANAGEMENT CO.___ and ___Annie B. Student___, hereinafter called respectively lessor and lessee.

WITNESSETH: That for and in consideration of the payment of the rents and the performance of the covenants contained on the part of lessee, said lessor does hereby demise and let unto the lessee, and lessee hires from lessor for use as a

residence those premises described as___Apartment #111___

located at___14777 Portsmouth Place___ Street, ___Los Angeles___, California, for a

tenancy from month-to-month commencing on the___1st___ day of ___October___, 19__96__, and

at a monthly rental of ___Four hundred and fifty___ ----------------------- ($___450.00___) Dollars per month,

payable monthly in advance on the___1st___ day of each and every month.

It is further mutually agreed between the parties as follows:

(1) Said premises shall be occupied by no more than___1___ adults and ___0___ children.

(2) Lessee shall not keep or permit to be kept in said premises any dog, cat, parrot, or other bird or animal.

(3) Lessee shall not violate any city ordinance or state law in or about said premises.

(4) That all alterations, additions, or improvements made in and to said premises shall, unless otherwise provided by written agreement between the parties hereto, be the property of Lessor and shall remain upon and be surrendered with the premises.

(5) Lessee shall not sub-let the demised premises, or any part thereof, or assign this agreement without the lessor's written consent.

(6) Any failure by lessee to pay rent or other charges promptly when due, or to comply with any other term or condition hereof, shall at the option of the lessor, and after lawful notice given, forthwith terminate this tenancy.

(7) Lessee shall keep and maintain the premises in a clean and sanitary condition at all times, and upon the termination of the tenancy shall surrender the premises to the lessor in as good condition as when received, ordinary wear and damage by the elements excepted.

(8) Except as to any condition which makes the premises untenantable, lessee hereby waives all right to make repairs at the expense of lessor as provided in Section 1942 of the Civil Code of the State of California, and all rights provided in Section 1941 of said Civil Code.

(9) The ___lessor___ agrees to properly cultivate, care for, and adequately water the lawn, shrubbery, trees and grounds.

(10) The ___lessor___ shall pay for all water supplied to the said premises. The lessee shall pay for all gas, heat, light, power, telephone service, and all other services, except as herein provided, supplied to the said premises.

(11) Nothing contained in this agreement shall be construed as waiving any of lessor's rights under the laws of the State of California.

(12) This agreement and the tenancy hereby granted may be terminated at any time by either party hereto by giving to the other party not less than

___thirty___ (___30___) days prior notice in writing.

(13) The prevailing party in an action brought for the recovery of rent or other moneys due or to become due under this lease or by reason of a breach of any covenant herein contained or for the recovery of the possession of said premises, or to compel the performance of anything agreed to be done herein, or to recover for damages to said property, or to enjoin any act contrary to the provisions hereof, shall be awarded all of the costs in connection therewith, including, but not by way of limitation, reasonable attorney's fees.

(14) Remarks: Security deposit $400.00 (refundable within 30 days of moving)
Cleaning fee $50.00 (not refundable)

IN WITNESS WHEREOF the parties hereto have executed this agreement in duplicate the day and year first above written.

M. Simon, Mgr. (for Total Control Mgmt. Co.)
Lessor

Annie B. Student
Lessee

Courtesy of Wolcotts, Inc.

1. What is the minimum amount of money it will cost Annie to move into her new apartment? Explain.

_____

_____

2. What is the term of the lease?

_____

_____

_____

3. To reduce expenses, Annie would like to share her apartment with a friend. According to her lease, can she? Why or why not?

_____

_____

_____

4. A mid-December heat wave causes Annie to use the air conditioner for a solid week. As a result, the bimonthly electric bill is doubled. Who pays the increase? Why?

_____

_____

_____

5. The garbage disposal breaks down, clogging the kitchen sink. It is the manager's day off.

   a. Rather than wait, Annie pays a plumber to fix the disposal. She withholds the cost of the repair from her next rent check. The manager demands full payment of the rent. Who is right? Why?

   _____

   _____

   _____

   _____

   _____

   b. Suppose that instead of making the repair herself, Annie asks the manager to handle it. Suppose, in addition, it takes two weeks to get a plumber. Is Annie entitled to a rent reduction? Why or why not?

   _____

   _____

   _____

   c. Suppose the problem is with the toilet rather than the kitchen sink. Would this fact change the results in either case? Why or why not?

   _____

   _____

   _____

   _____

Chapter **31** *Buying a House*

REVIEWING CONSUMER TERMS

Using the terms below, write a paragraph about buying a house.

appraisal

contract for sale

deed

escrow account

fixed-rate mortgage

mortgage

points

promissory note

variable-rate mortgage

_____

_____

_____

_____

_____

_____

_____

_____

_____

_____

_____

_____

_____

_____

_____

_____

_____

_____

_____

_____

_____

_____

_____

_____

_____

_____

_____

_____

Chapter **31** *Buying a House*

REVIEWING FACTS AND IDEAS

1. Cite the advantages of home ownership.

_____

_____

_____

_____

_____

_____

2. List the usual costs and procedures in buying a home.

_____

_____

_____

_____

_____

_____

3. What are the differences between a fixed-rate mortgage and a variable-rate mortgage?

_____

_____

_____

_____

_____

_____

4. What are the steps in inspecting a home?

_____

_____

_____

_____

_____

_____

Chapter 31 Buying a House

APPLICATION ACTIVITY 1

A mortgage is basically an installment contract for a house. The buyer agrees to make a certain number of payments over a certain number of years until the purchase price is paid in full.

1. Each mortgage payment includes interest (the finance charge) and principal (that portion of the purchase price remaining after the down payment has been made). Assume you need $100,000 to buy a home. The chart below represents your full range of mortgage options at 10 percent interest.

Down Payment	Loan Principal	Monthly Payment (in dollars)			Total Interest (in dollars)		
		15 yrs.	20 yrs.	25 yrs.	15 yrs.	20 yrs.	25 yrs.
0	100,000	1,075	965	909	93,500	131,600	172,700
5,000	95,000	1,021	917	863	88,780	125,080	163,900
10,000	90,000	967	869	818	84,060	118,560	155,400
15,000	85,000	913	820	772	79,340	111,800	146,600
20,000	80,000	860	772	727	74,800	105,280	138,100
25,000	75,000	806	724	682	70,080	98,760	129,600
30,000	70,000	752	676	636	65,360	92,240	120,800
35,000	65,000	698	627	591	60,640	85,480	112,300
40,000	60,000	645	579	545	56,100	78,960	103,500
45,000	55,000	591	531	500	51,380	72,440	95,000
50,000	50,000	537	483	454	46,660	65,920	86,200

a. Assume you have saved $20,000 for a down payment. What will your monthly payment be for each of the following mortgage terms?

15 yrs. _____   20 yrs. _____   25 yrs. _____

b. What relationship exists between mortgage term and size of monthly payment?

_____

c. Suppose you had saved only $10,000 for a down payment. What would your monthly payments be?

15 yrs. _____   20 yrs. _____   25 yrs. _____

d. What relationship exists between size of down payment and size of monthly payment?

_____

e. Assume you put $5,000 down and sign a 25-year mortgage at 10 percent. At the end of the mortgage term, how much will you actually have paid for the house?

_____

_____

f. What does buying a house on credit do to the purchase price?

_____

2. The preceding questions were based on a conventional mortgage (one having a fixed interest rate and a fixed monthly payment for its full term). Today this kind of financing is often not available to home buyers. Most must settle for variable-rate arrangements like the one summarized below.

House price .... $54,490 Down payment .... −3,690 Mortgage amount $50,800	APR: 10.06% including mortgage insurance	
Year	**Monthly payment**	**Annual payment**
1	$ 356.34	
2	367.03	
3	378.04	
4	389.88	
5	401.06	
6	413.09	
7	425.45	
8	438.25	
9	451.40	
10	464.94	
11-30	478.89	

a. Name the specific type of variable-rate mortgage described in the chart.

_____

_____

_____

_____

b. How long will it take a home buyer to pay off the mortgage?

_____

_____

_____

_____

c. Complete the chart by computing the total amount a home buyer must pay each year under the provisions of this mortgage.

d. At the end of the mortgage term, how much will the house have cost its new owner?

_____

_____

_____

_____

_____

Chapter **31** *Buying a House*

APPLICATION ACTIVITY 2

Floor plans for two houses appear below and on the next page. The first, the Monticello, is a single-family dwelling. The second, the Blair, is a townhouse. Study the two sets of floor plans and try to imagine what it would be like to live in each house. Consider room size, layout, storage space, kitchen and bath facilities, and any other features that would be important to you.

1. Summarize your opinions by listing the good and bad features of each house.

The MONTICELLO
A Prestige Residence

- Full basement
- Forced-air natural gas heating
- Professionally landscaped site with full cement driveway
- Wall-to-wall nylon carpeting (vinyl in kitchen, baths, foyer)

- Fiberglass insulation in ceilings and all exterior walls; three-track aluminum storm windows
- Forty gallon glass-lined water heater

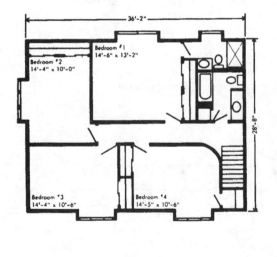

UPPER LEVEL

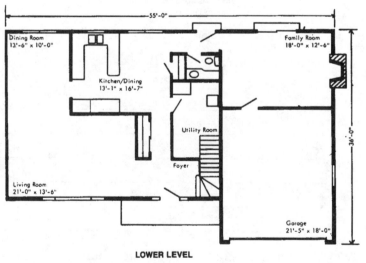

LOWER LEVEL

<table>
<tr><td align="center">**Good Features**</td><td align="center">**Bad Features**</td></tr>
<tr><td>_____</td><td>_____</td></tr>
<tr><td>_____</td><td>_____</td></tr>
<tr><td>_____</td><td>_____</td></tr>
<tr><td>_____</td><td>_____</td></tr>
<tr><td>_____</td><td>_____</td></tr>
</table>

The BLAIR

A Distinctive Town Home

- Full basement
- Natural gas heat and central air conditioning
- Fenced-in patios

- Wall-to-wall carpeting, custom drapes, and wallpaper
- Dishwasher, self-cleaning oven, and garbage disposal
- Ceramic tile in baths

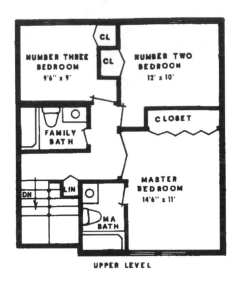

UPPER LEVEL

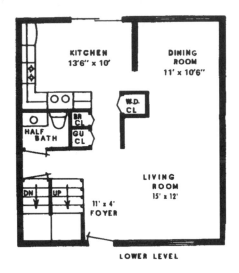

LOWER LEVEL

Good Features

_____

_____

_____

_____

_____

_____

Bad Features

_____

_____

_____

_____

_____

_____

2. Which house would your prefer for yourself and your family? Why? (Note: If neither is suitable, describe the features you would want in a house.)

_____

_____

_____

_____

_____

_____

_____

_____

CHAPTER **32** *Furnishing a Home*

REVIEWING CONSUMER TERMS

Create a collage, using photos from magazines and your own drawings, that depicts each of the terms below. Define each term below its illustration.

case goods

EnergyGuide

floor plan

hardwoods

particle board

softwoods

warranty

_____

_____

_____

_____

_____

_____

_____

_____

_____

_____

_____

_____

_____

_____

_____

_____

_____

_____

_____

_____

_____

_____

_____

_____

_____

_____

_____

_____

CHAPTER **32** *Furnishing a Home*

REVIEWING FACTS AND IDEAS

1. What are three major steps in planning an interior?

   _____

   _____

   _____

2. How would you go about inspecting a three-drawer chest for quality?

   _____

   _____

   _____

3. What are some common features you should investigate when buying a sofa and a bed?

   _____

   _____

   _____

4. Identify four indications of quality that you should look for when selecting a new appliance.

   _____

   _____

   _____

5. How does an implied warranty differ from a written warranty?

   _____

   _____

   _____

6. What kind of information do EnergyGuide labels provide?

   _____

   _____

   _____

7. What records should be kept on appliance purchases and why?

   _____

   _____

   _____

Copyright © Glencoe/McGraw-Hill

CHAPTER 32 *Furnishing a Home*

APPLICATION ACTIVITY 1

Your parents have just finished their basement and turned it into a recreation room. The only furniture they have for the room is a sofa bed that they're moving from the family room. Since one of the uses of the new room is for you to entertain friends, your parents have asked you for ideas about other furnishings. Study the floor plan below, then answer the questions that follow.

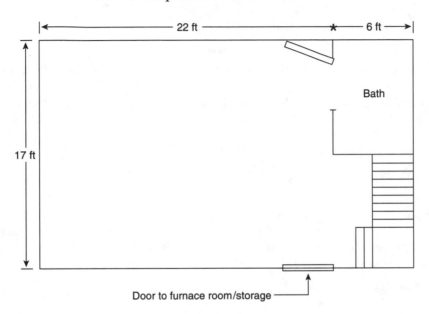

Door to furnace room/storage

1. List the ways in which you plan to use the new room.

   _____

   _____

2. What furnishings would be needed so you could use the room as listed in question 1?

   _____

   _____

   _____

3. Make a list below of the furnishings you would like for the room. Go to a local furniture, department, or appliance store and price the items on your list. Price economy brands as well as mid-priced brands.

Item	Economy Price	Mid-Level Price

4. When you price the items on your list from question 3, also write the dimensions of each item, such as tables, chairs, television, stereo stands, and so on. Write the dimensions in the space below.

Item	Dimensions
_____	_____
_____	_____
_____	_____
_____	_____
_____	_____
_____	_____

5. Now use the dimensions of the furnishings to plan how you would arrange them in the room. Draw the room on graph paper. Use a scale such as one-quarter inch (or one square on the paper) equal to a foot. After completing your floor plan, did all the furnishings fit that you wanted to use? What problems did you have in fitting items in the room? Did you have to omit some items?

_____

_____

_____

6. Now add the prices for all the items that you want to use in the room (and that will fit). Your parents have a budget in mind for furnishing this room, and your plans will most likely exceed that budget. Before discussing your ideas with your parents, list the items you want by priority with the most important ones at the top of your list. Write the price of each beside it.

Furnishings Priorities

a. _____   e. _____

b. _____   f. _____

c. _____   g. _____

d. _____   h. _____

7. To prepare for presenting your ideas to your parents and negotiate for the furnishings that you would like to have, create different combinations of furnishings at three different budget levels: low, medium, high (all the items on your list).

Low Budget	Medium Budget	High Budget
_____	_____	_____
_____	_____	_____
_____	_____	_____
_____	_____	_____
_____	_____	_____

8. Assume that you presented your plans to your parents and they agreed to the cost on your medium budget. Look at your lists again. Which items could you trade from one list to the other (for example, a lower priced television for a higher priced stereo) to furnish the room as you would like?

_____

_____

CHAPTER  *Furnishing a Home*

APPLICATION ACTIVITY 2

You belong to a small band that plays for dances and school activities. Your parents just gave you a new electronic keyboard for your birthday. The keyboard is made by the Matsuda Company and comes with an eight-page Owner's Manual, which contains the following statement. Read it carefully. Then answer the questions.

LIMITED WARRANTY

Matsuda Corporation warrants that this electronic keyboard is and shall remain free of defects in materials and workmanship for a period of one year from the date of original purchase. This warranty excludes damage or wear resulting from accident, abuse, tampering, unauthorized repair, power surges, or failure to follow the Standard Operating Instructions listed in the Owner's Manual.

If your electronic keyboard fails to operate under normal use conditions within the warranty period, Matsuda will repair or replace it at their discretion. Repairs will be made using new or thoroughly reconditioned parts, also at Matsuda's discretion.

Send the product, shipping charges prepaid, to Matsuda Corporation, 348 Wilson Drive, Kenosha, WI 53142, or hand carry it to your nearest Matsuda-approved service center (see page 5 of your Owner's Manual). If shipping, include a note stating your name and address, the nature of the defect or malfunction, and the date of purchase. NOTE: Matsuda will not be responsible for shipping damage. Therefore, when sending your product for service, use a sturdy box, pack securely, and insure your package against damage or loss in transit.

No charge will be made for repairs to defective parts under this warranty. Before authorizing or completing such repairs, however, Matsuda may require proof of purchase in the form of an original sales receipt or copy thereof. A minimum period of six to eight weeks shall be deemed reasonable for all repairs. Any return shipping charges will be borne by Matsuda.

The remedies described in this warranty are exclusive. Matsuda shall not be liable for indirect or consequential damages.

This warranty gives you specific legal rights. You may, however, have other rights which vary from state to state. Some states do not allow limitations on how long an implied warranty lasts or on indirect or consequential damages. Therefore, the above limitations or exclusions may not apply to you.

---

1. What kind of warranty is given on the electronic keyboard? Underline the provisions that you think account for this description.

_____

_____

_____

_____

_____

_____

2. Against what types of problems is the owner protected?

_____

_____

_____

3. What types of problems are specifically excluded from warranty protection?

_____

_____

_____

4. What is the length of the warranty? _____

5. What remedies are available to the purchaser of a defective keyboard?

_____

_____

6. Analyze these situations in the light of warranty provisions. In each case, state the probable outcome.

   a. When you set your keyboard to play accompanying drums, you get a humming noise but no drums. For repair, you return the keyboard to the dealer from whom it was purchased.

   _____

   _____

   b. Instead of taking your electronic keyboard to a service center, you mail it COD to the address given in the warranty.

   _____

   _____

   c. A relative has a small electronic repair business. You take the keyboard to her for repair. After three weeks of trying, she cannot find and fix the problem.

   _____

   _____

   d. You do not like the idea of Matsuda using reconditioned parts for repairs. You send the keyboard (postage paid) to Kenosha, but in your letter you request that only new parts be used as replacements.

   _____

   _____

   e. You use a private parcel service to send your keyboard to Kenosha. You pack the keyboard carefully and accept the standard insurance of $100. During the trip to Kenosha, a heavy box fell on your package and crushed it.

   _____

   _____

   f. The plug on your keyboard proves to be defective. The result is a small fire and a large bill for rewiring the wall outlet.

   _____

   _____

   _____

   _____

UNIT **10** *LAB Selecting Housing*

CHOOSING A PLACE TO LIVE

Unit 10 focuses on one of the most important decisions a person makes—selecting housing. This lab will allow you to study the housing selection process more closely. In this lab, you will also select a personal computer.

TOOLS
1. Newspapers
2. Government pamphlets

PROCEDURES
Read the lab in your textbook and complete each activity using the space provided below.

Step A
Possible leases (address/name and telephone number of person to contact/price):

1. _____
2. _____
3. _____
4. _____
5. _____

Possible purchases (address/name and telephone number of person to contact/price):

1. _____
2. _____
3. _____
4. _____
5. _____

Step B
Real estate agent: _____
Telephone number: _____

Step C
Use separate paper to make a chart of the features, disadvantages, and the lease payment or estimated mortgage payment for each property listed in Step B.

LAB REPORT
Step D

Using your charts and the notes from your conversations with the real estate agent answer the following questions.

1. If your relatives made a $20,000 down payment on the house that you feel would best suit their needs, how much money would they have to borrow to meet the current asking price for the house?

   _____

   _____

   _____

   a. If your relatives borrowed the money at the average fixed rate, what would be their monthly mortgage payment?

   _____

   _____

   _____

   b. What would the payment be if they borrowed at the adjustable rate?

   _____

   c. What is the difference between the payments you noted in a and b above? What accounts for this difference?

   _____

   _____

   _____

   _____

2. What is the difference between the average mortgage payment on the three houses that are for sale and the average rent on the three houses that are for lease?

   _____

   _____

   _____

Step E

Using a word processor or a typewriter, write a two-page report explaining the choice between leasing and buying a house in terms of economic and psychological trade-offs and benefits.

UNIT 11 Using Professional Services

ATTITUDE INVENTORY

Before you begin Unit 11, take stock of your attitudes by completing the following inventory. Read each statement and decide how you feel about it—agree, disagree, or undecided. Write your answers in the blanks.

1. Only people over 21 who have children are likely to use professional services.

    1. _____

2. Routine physical examinations are important even after a person is no longer subject to childhood diseases.

    2. _____

3. Dental examinations are not important after a person reaches adulthood.

    3. _____

4. Consulting the Yellow Pages is probably the best way to select a doctor.

    4. _____

5. Medical care should be financed from savings on an emergency-by-emergency basis rather than included as a regular budget item.

    5. _____

6. It shows poor taste to ask in advance what a medical service will cost.

    6. _____

7. The medical field has not been affected by inflation.

    7. _____

8. Medicare has solved all the medical problems of older citizens.

    8. _____

9. The local bar association knows best when it comes to matching specific attorneys with specific clients.

    9. _____

10. There are not enough medical doctors in the United States.

    10. _____

11. Legal firms in large cities usually charge more for services than legal firms in small towns.

    11. _____

12 Poor people can secure legal advice from well-qualified professionals free of charge.

    12. _____

13. Legal insurance is nothing more than a scheme to get money from the consumer and give nothing in return.

    13. _____

RECHECKING YOUR ATTITUDE

Before going on to the next unit, answer the Attitude Inventory questions a second time. Then compare the two sets of responses. On how many statements have your attitudes changed? Can you account for these shifts in your opinions? What do you know now that you did not know then?

1. Only people over 21 who have children are likely to use professional services.

1. _____

2. Routine physical examinations are important even after a person is no longer subject to childhood diseases.

2. _____

3. Dental examinations are not important after a person reaches adulthood.

3. _____

4. Consulting the Yellow Pages is probably the best way to select a doctor.

4. _____

5. Medical care should be financed from savings on an emergency-by-emergency basis rather than included as a regular budget item.

5. _____

6. It shows poor taste to ask in advance what a medical service will cost.

6. _____

7. The medical field has not been affected by inflation.

7. _____

8. Medicare has solved all the medical problems of older citizens.

8. _____

9. The local bar association knows best when it comes to matching specific attorneys with specific clients.

9. _____

10. There are not enough medical doctors in the United States.

11. Legal firms in large cities usually charge more for services than legal firms in small towns.

10. _____

11. _____

12 Poor people can secure legal advice from well-qualified professionals free of charge.

12. _____

13. Legal insurance is nothing more than a scheme to get money from the consumer and give nothing in return.

13. _____

Answers changed _____Why? _____

_____

_____

_____

_____

_____

_____

_____

_____

_____

_____

_____

_____

_____

_____

CHAPTER **33** *Medical and Dental Services*

REVIEWING CONSUMER TERMS

Use the following terms in a paragraph to demonstrate you know their meaning.

prenatal care
preventive medicine

CHAPTER 33 *Medical and Dental Services*

REVIEWING FACTS AND IDEAS

1. List at least five important ways to practice preventive medicine.

   _____

   _____

   _____

   _____

   _____

   _____

   _____

   _____

2. Tell how you would go about choosing a physician after moving to a different city or town.

   _____

   _____

   _____

   _____

   _____

   _____

   _____

   _____

   _____

3. What steps can consumers take to reduce health care costs?

   _____

   _____

   _____

   _____

   _____

   _____

   _____

   _____

   _____

   _____

CHAPTER 33 *Medical and Dental Services*

APPLICATION ACTIVITY 1

In the last several years, the cost of medical and dental care has become an increasingly important consumer issue. To understand why, complete the tables below and answer the questions that follow.

SELECTED PER CAPITA HEALTH CARE EXPENDITURES						
Item	1970	1980	% Increase (1970–1980)	1990	% Increase (1980–1990)	% Increase (1970–90)
Physicians' services	$63	$178		$496		
Dentists' services	$22	$61		$131		
Other professional health care services	$7	$37		$118		

1. Compute the percentage increase in expenditures for each category and each time period shown. Write your answers in the table.

2. What has happened to doctors' bills since 1970? Describe the trend.

   _____

   _____

   _____

   _____

3. Have dentists' fees matched this pace? Explain.

   _____

   _____

   _____

4. In which ten-year period did all three expenditure categories increase more? What do you think this fact means for the future?

   _____

   _____

   _____

   _____

5. For the past two decades, increases in health-care costs have outpaced increases in most other components of the Consumer Price Index. Why are consumer groups and some government officials alarmed?

   _____

   _____

   _____

   _____

   _____

CHAPTER  Medical and Dental Services

APPLICATION ACTIVITY 2

Until a few years ago, most insurance companies would not pay for an operation unless it was done in a hospital. Today many companies will not pay for certain operations unless they are performed on an out-patient basis. The main reason, as the table below shows, is cost.

Operation	In-Patient Cost ($)	Out-Patient Cost ($)	Difference	
			$	%
A	800	500		
B	900	390		
C	700	380		

1. How much would you save by having each of the listed operations done on an out-patient basis? Compute both dollar amounts and percentage savings (using the in-patient costs). Write your answers in the table.

2. Using the data in the table, generalize about how much on the average a patient can save by having surgery done on an outpatient basis.

   _____

   _____

3. Would you be willing to have an operation on an out-patient basis? Under what circumstances?

   _____

   _____

4. You must have some dental work done. The table below lists the prices quoted to you from two sources—your family dentist and a dental clinic located in a nearby shopping mall.

Service	Cost: Family Dentist	Cost: Mall Clinic	Difference	
			$	%
A	$90	$59		
B	$50	$35		
C	$534	$300		

   a. How much would you save by going to the clinic instead of your family dentist? Compute both dollar amounts and percentage savings (compute percentages based on family dentist figures). Write your answers in the table.

   b. What factors besides cost might you consider in reaching a decision?

   _____

   _____

CHAPTER **34** *Legal Services*

REVIEWING CONSUMER TERMS

Use the following terms in a paragraph about the legal profession.

bar association
contingency basis
contract

legal counsel
Martindale-Hubbell Law Directory
pro bono work

_____

_____

_____

_____

_____

_____

_____

_____

_____

_____

_____

_____

_____

_____

_____

_____

_____

_____

_____

_____

_____

_____

_____

_____

_____

_____

_____

_____

Chapter **34** _Legal Services_

REVIEWING FACTS AND IDEAS

1. If you needed a lawyer, how would you go about choosing one?

   _____

   _____

   _____

   _____

   _____

   _____

2. What do legal ethics require of attorneys?

   _____

   _____

   _____

   _____

   _____

3. Why do many consumers fail to seek out legal counsel when they have legal problems?

   _____

   _____

   _____

   _____

   _____

4. What can people do to reduce the high costs of legal services?

   _____

   _____

   _____

   _____

   _____

CHAPTER 34 *Legal Services*

APPLICATION ACTIVITY 1

The article below first appeared in print when legal clinics were just becoming popular. It continues to be one of the best descriptions of legal clinic services. Read the article, then answer the questions on the next page.

JUDGING LEGAL CLINICS

By Andrea Pawlyna

If your legal problem is fairly simple—you want a will written or you and your husband are filing for an uncontested divorce—a legal clinic may be a good option for you.

Often located in shopping centers, these storefront sources of legal advice specialize in handling routine matters of law. Because they operate on a high-volume, high-efficiency basis, clinics generally charge their clients lower fees than traditional law firms.

Since the landmark Supreme Court ruling in 1977 allowing lawyers to advertise, the number of legal clinics has mushroomed from a mere handful to over 600 firms nationwide, according to a new study by the American Bar Association (ABA).

Types of clinics can range from solo practitioners in single offices to large multistate chains. Many clinics build case volume through advertising, and all commonly set fixed prices for such standard legal work as bankruptcies, simple wills, real estate closings, adoptions and uncontested divorces.

"What we offer is the general practice of law covering the majority of consumer problems," says 32-year-old Linda Hawley, co-founder of Cawley & Schmidt legal clinics, a Baltimore-based chain which has nine local offices in Maryland and New York.

Cawley & Schmidt charges $50 for a simple will, $150 for an uncontested divorce and $250 for a real estate settlement An initial consultation is free. "We lose a third of our clients by being able to dispose of the problem right away," adds Rich Schmidt, 32. "But the free visit generates goodwill, so we've continued doing it."

By streamlining their operations, clinics are able to keep fees low. In many offices, standardized legal forms and computers speed case work along.

While clinics once tried to gear themselves to the wage earner not far above the poverty level, lately their focus has changed. "At first, they were serving the person who couldn't quite qualify for Legal Aid. But they found out that business wasn't all that profitable. Now the trend is toward a more middle-class clientele," says Bill Bolger, a spokesman for the Washington-based National Resource Center for Consumers of Legal Service.

As part of their upscale image, some firms are shedding the word "clinic" from their names. The term apparently had caused a certain degree of confusion, leading some people to mistakenly assume that clinics were either free or offered only the most limited type of legal Service.

In still another wrinkle, Hyatt Legal Services, a 45-clinic chain based in Kansas City, Missouri, has joined with H & R Block (the income tax preparers) to establish what may become the first truly national chain of legal clinics.

How good are legal clinics? Though they were at first criticized by local Bar associations, which warned that they would lower the quality of service, that does not appear to have happened. A study by the University of Miami School of Law indicates just the opposite. Clinic clients reported more satisfaction with their attorneys than did clients of traditional firms.

Experts usually recommend clinics for simple legal cases, but they caution that even the best may be ill-equipped to handle matters involving large property claims, sizable estates or divorces.

Before choosing a legal clinic, it's wise for consumers to comparison shop for the best deal since even clinic prices tend to vary widely. The ABA, for example, found that fees for uncontested divorces range from $50 to $550, while a simple will can cost anywhere from $20 to $100.

"Listen to the advertising," advises Bolger. "Visit the clinic and ask about the fee, and also find out about the experience of the lawyer who will be handling your case."

Reprinted from Family Weekly, copyright 1982, 1515 Broadway, New York, NY 10036.

1. What type of problems do legal clinics normally handle? What do all of these problems have in common?

   _____

   _____

   _____

   _____

2. How can legal clinics afford to charge lower fees than private attorneys?

   _____

   _____

   _____

3. a. Why is advertising so important to legal clinics?

   _____

   _____

   _____

   _____

   b. To what group do most legal clinics direct their advertising? Why?

   _____

   _____

   _____

4. a. Why are some legal clinics dropping the word clinic from their names?

   _____

   _____

   _____

   b. What kinds of terms are they substituting? (In other words, how can consumers tell a legal clinic from a traditional law firm on the basis of name alone?)

   _____

   _____

   _____

5. How would you go about choosing a legal clinic for yourself?

   _____

   _____

   _____

   _____

   _____

CHAPTER **34** *Legal Services*

APPLICATION ACTIVITY 2

The situations described below and on the next page present cases in which there is a need for legal assistance. For each situation, decide which type of legal assistance would be better: the services of a private attorney or the use of a legal services firm (clinic). Explain the reason for your choice in each situation.

1. Jaime and Maria Sulena have purchased a house. They are first-time home buyers. The closing for their home purchase is to be held next week. They would like someone to review the documents that they will be signing at the closing.

_____

_____

_____

_____

_____

2. Kevin Martin was involved in an auto accident, which he caused when he failed to stop at a traffic signal. Kevin and his insurance company are being sued by the other party in the accident. The insurance company has an attorney who will handle their responses to the suit.

_____

_____

_____

_____

_____

3. Carla and Harry Nelson have been married for five years. Last year, Harry moved into a separate apartment, and Carla stayed in the one they had been renting. The couple have no children. Carla and Harry have agreed to file for a divorce.

_____

_____

_____

_____

4. Wanda Palinsky has agreed to sell twenty acres of land to her next-door neighbor. No real estate agent is involved in the sale. Wanda needs someone to write a contract of sale and prepare a deed transferring the ownership of the property.

_____

_____

_____

_____

_____

5. The Marsite Development Corporation has made an offer to buy your property. The company plans to buy the property belonging to several of your neighbors as well. Their offer to you is contingent on their being able also to buy the surrounding land.

_____

_____

_____

_____

_____

6. Jason and Janice Balthas have been married for nine years. They have two children and own a three-bedroom home, two cars, and a time-share vacation property. Jason and Janice have agreed to file for divorce and to work out the issue of child custody and visitation rights.

_____

_____

_____

_____

_____

7. Marty and Jennifer Houston have one child and plan to have other children in the future. They are making payments on a home and a car. Although they are both young and in good health, the Houstons want to have wills prepared. Their wills would specify a guardian for their child should they both die before the child reaches adulthood.

_____

_____

_____

_____

_____

8. Until last year, you worked for the Bender Company. The company filed for bankruptcy, and company officials announced that the company-sponsored pension plan was not fully funded. Bender had not made their matching contributions to the plan for the past two years, and the money that employees had contributed had been used by the company to pay its operating expenses.

_____

_____

_____

_____

_____

_____

UNIT 11 LAB Using Professional Services

RESEARCHING CONSUMER ISSUES AND THE MEDICAL PROFESSION

Unit 11 discusses the consumer issues that have an impact on the medical, dental, and legal professions. In this lab, you will learn how the cost of medical care influences doctors, hospitals, and patients.

TOOLS

1. News magazines and newspapers
2. Consumer magazines
3. Literature from hospitals and health maintenance and preferred provider organizations
4. Literature from medical and dental schools

PROCEDURES

Read the lab in your textbook and complete each activity using the space provided below.

Step A

Interview questions:

_____

_____

_____

_____

_____

_____

_____

Step B

Health-care professional #1: _____

Telephone number: _____

Health-care professional #2: _____

Telephone number: _____

Health-care professional #3: _____

Telephone number: _____

Step C

Interview questions:

_____

_____

_____

_____

_____

_____

_____

_____

_____

_____

_____

Step D

Hospital administrative employee: _____

Telephone number: _____

Name of hospital: _____

LAB REPORT

Step E

Use your interview notes to answer the questions below.

1. What was the monetary difference between the fee charged for an office visit by a doctor in private practice and by one in an HMO?

   _____

2. What percentage of a routine dental cleaning and checkup is usually the patient's responsibility?

   _____

3. What is the cost difference between room and board for a private room and for one shared by four patients?

   _____

4. What accounts for the costs of an intensive care or cardiac care unit room?

   _____

   _____

5. During the last five years, what actions have medical professionals and hospitals taken to lower costs, and how successful have their efforts been?

   _____

   _____

Step F

Using a word processor or a typewriter, write a two-page report explaining how the rising costs of medical care and medical insurance have had an impact on the availability of medical care.

UNIT 12 Social Responsibility

ATTITUDE INVENTORY

Before you begin Unit 12, take stock of your attitudes by completing the following inventory. Read each statement and decide how you feel about it—agree, disagree, or undecided. Write your answers in the blanks.

1. Shoplifting is a consumer problem, not just a problem for store owners.

    1. _____

2. Character traits of a good citizen are as good an indicator of success in life as a high IQ.

    2. _____

3. Recycling not only conserves resources, it reduces pollution and often saves money.

    3. _____

4. A simple way to help reduce pollution at home is to use gas lawnmowers.

    4. _____

5. Just as kinder and gentler types of personalities are being defined, the numbers of people with these characteristics are increasing.

    5. _____

6. People are born with characteristics of a good citizen; these characteristics cannot be taught.

    6. _____

7. Many ecological problems relate to the production and use of energy.

    7. _____

8. Conservation of natural resources is a recent concern.

    8. _____

9. Volunteers are not needed as much today because government resources provide needed services.

    9. _____

10. Vandalism is often the beginning of crime in neighborhoods.

    10. _____

11. Leadership can occur behind the scenes.

    11. _____

12. Taxpayers give up personal purchases for public services that benefit the community.

    12. _____

13. Many groups have been formed to protect the environment—there is little individuals can do.

    13. _____

14. Conflicting societal goals make some actions to preserve the environment controversial.

    14. _____

15. It is important to compare several sources of information and look at the entire picture when trying to preserve the environment.

    15. _____

16. Heating and cooling a home uses about half of your energy resources.

    16. _____

RECHECKING YOUR ATTITUDE

Answer the Attitude Inventory questions for Unit 12 a second time. Then compare the two sets of responses. On how many statements have your attitudes changed? Can you account for these shifts in your opinions? What do you know now that you did not know then?

1. Shoplifting is a consumer problem, not just a problem for store owners.

1. _____

2. Character traits of a good citizen are as good an indicator of success in life as a high IQ.

2. _____

3. Recycling not only conserves resources, it reduces pollution and often saves money.

3. _____

4. A simple way to help reduce pollution at home is to use gas lawnmowers.

4. _____

5. Just as kinder and gentler types of personalities are being defined, the numbers of people with these characteristics are increasing.

5. _____

6. People are born with characteristics of a good citizen; these characteristics cannot be taught.

6. _____

7. Many ecological problems relate to the production and use of energy.

7. _____

8. Conservation of natural resources is a recent concern.

8. _____

9. Volunteers are not needed as much today because government resources provide needed services.

9. _____

10. Vandalism is often the beginning of crime in neighborhoods.

10. _____

11. Leadership can occur behind the scenes.

11. _____

12. Taxpayers give up personal purchases for public services that benefit the community.

12. _____

13. Many groups have been formed to protect the environment—there is little individuals can do.

13. _____

14. Conflicting societal goals make some actions to preserve the environment controversial.

14. _____

15. It is important to compare several sources of information and look at the entire picture when trying to preserve the environment.

15. _____

16. Heating and cooling a home uses about half of your energy resources.

16. _____

Answers changed _____ Why? _____

_____

_____

_____

_____

_____

_____

_____

_____

_____

_____

CHAPTER 35 *Your Role As a Citizen*

REVIEWING CONSUMER TERMS

Use each of the following terms in a skit about your role as a citizen.

citizen   naturalization
ethics   vandalism
leadership   volunteer

_____
_____
_____
_____
_____
_____
_____
_____
_____
_____
_____
_____
_____
_____
_____
_____
_____
_____
_____
_____
_____
_____
_____
_____
_____
_____
_____

Name Class Date

CHAPTER 35 Your Role As a Citizen

REVIEWING FACTS AND IDEAS

1. How do communities and individuals benefit from good citizenship, and what are the characteristics of a good citizen?

2. What are some ways to be a good citizen at home? at school?

3. What are four roles of good citizens in the community?

4. Explain the difference between social and ethical responsibilities.

5. What are some characteristics of leadership roles?

CHAPTER 35 *Your Role As a Citizen*

APPLICATION ACTIVITY 1

Being a good citizen means different things to different people. Some people show good citizenship by donating to charities, while others do volunteer work in their communities. Read each situation described below, then describe the actions that you could take to demonstrate your own good citizenship.

1. Your mom must work extra hours to help with family living expenses.

_____

_____

_____

2. A new student at school does not know anyone and feels left out.

_____

_____

_____

3. Winter is coming and your town has housing enough for only 50 percent of the homeless people in your area.

_____

_____

_____

4. There is a vacant lot in your neighborhood that is available for a citizen project.

_____

_____

_____

5. There has been publicity about actions of a local elected official, and a recall election has been announced.

_____

_____

_____

6. A local park has become a dumping site for trash. Because of its bad condition, few people go there and now it is considered unsafe.

_____

_____

_____

7. Your neighborhood is becoming run down, with lots of homes needing repair.

_____

_____

_____

CHAPTER **35** *Your Role As a Citizen*

APPLICATION ACTIVITY 2

Read the summary of the news article below, then answer the questions that follow.

ACTIVIST SHAREHOLDERS

The nuns didn't plan it that way, but they ended up taking on the giant Anheuser-Busch company that produces Budweiser and other beers. Concerned that young people were being enticed into drinking by slick advertising, they joined groups that put pressure on the company to look at how its marketing is affecting young people. They also became activists through their stock portfolio, refusing to buy shares in tobacco and other companies.

The nuns try to make change by establishing cordial relations with company officials. One might assume that their target companies would become enemies, but that is not the case. This became clear when the sisters were protesting the presence of Coca-Cola in South Africa during the time of the apartheid government. When one of the sisters collapsed at a shareholders' meeting and had to be hospitalized, the company sent flowers. A company spokesperson said that they enjoyed the dialogue with the sisters.

Another project was taken on after a trip to the Dominican Republic. The sisters used a shareholders' meeting for Gulf and Western Industries, Inc. (now Paramount Communications, Inc.) to speak out about the poor working conditions they saw in the Dominican Republic. Eventually, the company began improving conditions there. While the nun's actions do not always get results, they do generate publicity that can help to bring about change.

1. How were the sisters being good citizens?

   _____

   _____

2. Why do you think the nuns continue to work toward social change even though it is often difficult to bring about change?

   _____

   _____

3. Why do you think it is better to address issues in a friendly manner?

   _____

   _____

4. What techniques did the sisters use to promote their ideas?

   _____

   _____

5. Why do you think the sisters usually worked within the structure of a group?

   _____

   _____

   _____

CHAPTER 36 You and the Environment

REVIEWING CONSUMER TERMS

Use each of the following terms in an essay about the environment.

conservation   nonrenewable resources
ecology   pollution
environmentalists   renewable resources
fossil fuels

_____

_____

_____

_____

_____

_____

_____

_____

_____

_____

_____

_____

_____

_____

_____

_____

_____

_____

_____

_____

_____

_____

_____

_____

_____

_____

_____

_____

CHAPTER 36 You and the Environment

REVIEWING FACTS AND IDEAS

1. What is the difference between renewable resources and nonrenewable resources?

_____

_____

_____

2. List four ecological problems related to the use and misuse of resources.

_____

_____

_____

_____

3. What two conflicting goals exist when trying to conserve resources?

_____

_____

_____

_____

4. Name four groups that often work on conserving resources and protecting the environment.

_____

_____

_____

_____

5. What are some things you can do at home to conserve energy and water?

_____

_____

_____

_____

6. List at least two things you can do at home to reduce waste and pollution.

_____

_____

_____

_____

CHAPTER 36 *You and the Environment*

APPLICATION ACTIVITY 1

There's a lot of controversy today about the environment. Are we damaging our future resources through pollution and overuse? Should we do more to protect the environment? Read each situation below, then decide what actions you can take to help protect or improve the environment.

1. You discover that in an average life of 75 years, a consumer will produce 52 tons of garbage. In general, what can you do to reduce the amount of garbage you create?

   _____

   _____

   _____

   _____

   _____

2. You have waste products such as lighter fluid, oil-based paint, and furniture polish that you want to discard.

   _____

   _____

   _____

   _____

3. You have too many magazines and catalogs at home.

   _____

   _____

   _____

4. It has been a hot, dry summer, and your community's water supply is very low.

   _____

   _____

   _____

   _____

5. Some products benefit the environment because they use less energy to operate or they can be reused instead of discarded. For example, fluorescent light bulbs use less electricity. List some other products that benefit the environment.

   _____

   _____

   _____

   _____

   _____

   _____

CHAPTER 36 *You and the Environment*

APPLICATION ACTIVITY 2

Read the following summary, then answer the questions below. Use the information in the summary as well as that in your textbook chapter.

Chlorofluorocarbons (CFCs) are chemical substances used in such products as refrigerants, aerosol propellants, plastic foam, and computer chip solvents. These chemicals destroy the ozone layer in the atmosphere, which leads to more cases of skin cancer and may have an impact on plants and, ultimately, the food supply. An international committee is working on drastically reducing or eliminating the use of CFCs by the end of the century. Several acceptable substitutes have already been developed for these chemicals, and most U.S. manufacturers have already stopped using CFCs in their products.

Another problem that affects the atmosphere is the greenhouse effect. When heat energy from the sun is trapped by ozone, water vapor, and carbon dioxide, the temperature of the earth is raised. The greenhouse effect is caused primarily by the burning of coal, oil, and natural gas. Environmentalists have a target of reducing greenhouse gases by 8 percent by the year 2000.

1. What are some common products that used CFCs either in their production or as an ingredient?

_____

_____

2. What are some specific ways that carbon dioxide is introduced into the atmosphere?

_____

_____

_____

3. What are some ways the government can encourage protection of the atmosphere?

_____

_____

_____

_____

_____

4. What are some things individuals can do to help protect the atmosphere?

_____

_____

_____

_____

_____

UNIT **12** *LAB Social Responsibility*

ADDRESSING A COMMUNITY NEED

Unit 12 addresses your role as a citizen and your responsibilities to the environment. In this lab, you will continue to investigate the impact that you and other citizens can have on your community and on the environment in which we all live.

TOOLS

1. Community newspapers and the community-focus sections of wide-circulation newspapers
2. Newsletters from political, social, and neighborhood groups
3. Literature from local chapters of volunteer political and social-action groups
4. Interviews with local businesspeople

PROCEDURES

Read the lab in your textbook and complete each activity using the space provided below.

Step A

Local official: _____

Telephone number: _____

Local official: _____

Telephone number: _____

Step B

Research Notes

_____

_____

_____

_____

_____

_____

_____

_____

_____

_____

_____

_____

_____

LAB REPORT
Step C

Use your interview and research notes to answer the questions below.

1. How many people will need to be involved in your project in order to get it established?

_____

2. What will be the role of each person?

_____

_____

3. What costs will be involved?

_____

4. What costs will be part of the continued operation of your project?

_____

5. How many people will need to be involved in the continuing operation of your project, and what will each person's role be?

_____

_____

6. How will the money be raised?

_____

_____

7. If donations will be a major source of money, who will the donors be and how much money will each donor need to contribute?

_____

_____

8. What financial impact will the project have on local businesses or local government?

_____

_____

Step D

Using a word processor or a typewriter, write a two-page report outlining the community need, and the benefits and costs of your project. Convince the reader of the need for your project and of its feasibility.